CONTENTS

Chapter 1 **GM Trends**

Chapter 2 **The Debate**

OTHER TITLES IN THE ISSUES SERIES

For more on these titles, visit: www.independence.co.uk

A note on critical evaluation

Because the information reprinted here is from a number of different sources, readers should bear in mind the origin of the text and whether the source is likely to have a particular bias when presenting information (just as they would if undertaking their own research). It is hoped that, as you read about the many aspects of the issues explored in this book, you will critically evaluate the information presented. It is important that you decide whether you are being presented with facts or opinions. Does the writer give a biased or an unbiased report? If an opinion is being expressed, do you agree with the writer?

Genetic Modification offers a useful starting point for those who need convenient access to information about the many issues involved. However, it is only a starting point. Following each article is a URL to the relevant organisation's website, which you may wish to visit for further information.

Genetic Modification

ISSUES

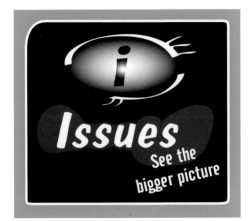

Volume 208

Series Editor

Lisa Firth

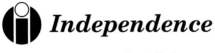

Independence

Educational Publishers

Cambridge

First published by Independence

The Studio, High Green

Great Shelford

Cambridge CB22 5EG

England

© Independence 2011

British Library Cataloguing in Publication Data
Genetic modification. -- (Issues ; v. 208)

1. Genetically modified foods. 2. Genetically modified

foods--Health aspects.

I. Series II. Firth, Lisa.

363.1'92-dc22

ISBN-13: 978 1 86168 584 1

Printed in Great Britain
MWL Print Group Ltd

The science behind GM crops

Information from the Agricultural Biotechnology Council.

What is GM?

'GM' stands for genetic modification. A gene is an instruction and each of our cells contains tens of thousands of these instructions.

For thousands of years farmers have selected plants with the characteristics they want, such as extra seeds in a pod or the ability to survive in the cold. By crossing the best plants, they hoped to produce even better varieties. But this approach is a bit like playing a fruit machine: you hit the jackpot only very occasionally.

On the other hand, GM allows chosen individual genes to be transferred from one organism into another, including genes between non-related species. Such methods can be used to create GM crop plants. The technology is also sometimes called 'modern biotechnology', 'gene technology', 'recombinant DNA technology' or 'genetic engineering'.

How is GM tested?

The testing process is rigorous and prescribed by law – initially, genetic modification is carried out in laboratories, growth chambers and greenhouses. This prevents contact between the GM plants and the environment.

When a suitable plant has been selected, it is grown in confined field plots to test whether its new trait works outside laboratory conditions and is stable. Researchers will then assess any potential effect on the environment, such as the plant cross-breeding with wild relatives and potential for weediness or damage to friendly insects.

Any GM foods intended for sale in the European Union are subject to a rigorous safety assessment which is the responsibility of the European Food Safety Authority (EFSA). However, the final decision for authorisation still rests with Member States, which vote on each GM food application as it arises. In the event of an inconclusive vote, the file is considered by the Council of Ministers; if there is no political consensus at this level, the final decision rests with the European Commission.

Case study: Uganda

Saving bananas from fungus

⇨ Black Sigatoka is a fungus causing a leaf spot disease in banana plants which reduces yields by 50% or more. The fungus has developed resistance to many fungicides so that, for effective control, more applications of more chemicals at higher strengths are needed; not counting the health and environmental issues, this can cost in excess of $1,000 per hectare, well beyond the reach of the African smallholder.

⇨ For today's Ugandan farmer, GM is the only rapid route to a resistant variety. GM plants were imported into Uganda in 2007 and are now being field tested.

What is available now and what can we expect in the future?

Three types of GM plants are currently being used or researched, described as 'generations':

First generation...

⇨ These plants have traits that help farmers to manage their land, increase their yields or reduce their costs; they are the GM crops currently widely planted throughout the world. Such plants are resistant to insect or virus attack (e.g. maize and papaya), or are tolerant of a particular weed killer (e.g. maize, cotton, soybean, oilseed rape), or both. GM research and plant trials are ongoing in Africa, Asia, Australasia, Europe, North and South America.

Initially, genetic modification is carried out in laboratories, growth chambers and greenhouses. This prevents contact between the GM plants and the environment

⇨ The first generation GM crops currently being grown around the world are: soybeans, maize, oilseed rape, cotton, sugar beet, papayas, tomatoes, peppers, alfalfa sprout, squash and flowers.

Second generation...

⇨ The second generation has traits that enhance the nutritional value of food and animal feed; these include maize and soya with increased levels of vitamins, amino acids or improved oil composition, together with drought tolerance traits.

Third generation...

⇨ Work on the third generation of GM crops is looking at how plants might be used as factories to make pharmaceutical products and renewable industrial compounds. Research is underway, for example, to produce edible vaccines within plants as a way of facilitating access to vaccines in countries where the distribution or refrigeration of medicines is poor.

What are the benefits of GM?

GM is being used by researchers to produce plants that can:

⇨ Increase crop yields, particularly where this maximises the plant's use of inputs such as fertiliser;

⇨ Reduce damage to crops after they are harvested by identifying natural genetic defences against insect damage and fungal contamination in foodstuffs;

⇨ Make crops more tolerant of stresses (cold, drought, salt, heat), traits that can be introduced from other plants that exhibit them;

⇨ Improve the nutritional value of food without changing other features;

⇨ Reduce reliance on spraying to control insects and diseases, by using genes available, for example, in soil microorganisms;

⇨ Reduce the carbon footprint of livestock farming by introducing changes in clover and grass so that cattle eating them produce less methane;

⇨ Provide alternative resources for industrial use by using plants (and therefore sunlight as the source of energy) to produce starches, fuels and pharmaceuticals – things that they could never be conventionally bred to produce;

⇨ All of these effects make farming more efficient and more productive, so keeping food prices down and helping farmers in poorer countries to make ends meet;

⇨ And, as we have seen, many of the consequences make agriculture more 'environmentally friendly'.

Is it safe to eat GM food?

After 13 years of being consumed by hundreds of millions of people, there is no substantiated evidence of any health effect from eating GM food products. In fact, the use of the more precise technology and the intense regulatory and scientific scrutiny arguably make GM products safer than conventional foods.

⇨ The above information is reprinted with kind permission from the Agricultural Biotechnology Council. Visit www.abcinformation.org for more information.

© *Agricultural Biotechnology Council 2009*

Potential risks and benefits of genetically modified crops

Benefits and potential benefits claimed by GM supporters	Potential risks claimed by GM opponents
Could help to feed the developing world	Will not be able to feed the world
GM crops are more cost-effective	Could damage organic farmers
Could benefit human health	May have unpredictable health risks
Could reduce pesticide and herbicide use	Could increase herbicide and pesticide use
Could help preserve natural habitats	Could reduce biodiversity
	Mainly benefits big biotech companies
	Raises ethical conflicts over the control of food production

Source: BioEthics Education Project (BEEP). www.beep.ac.uk

AGRICULTURAL BIOTECHNOLOGY COUNCIL

GM – the facts

Information from Debate Your Plate.

By Susan Tomlinson

What does GM mean?

These are foods that have had specific changes directly introduced to their DNA. This is different from plant breeding, or cross-pollinating – which has been happening for centuries. GM uses genetic engineering to create extremely precise changes to the actual cellular structure of the plant.

I think I'll do some planting today, so...I better ring my lawyers!

These changes include creating plants that are, for example, herbicide resistant, so farmers can spray as much herbicide as necessary to kill other pests and plants without damaging the plant. Another example of a GM seed is known as 'Bt', where the seed itself has been genetically altered to express a bacterial toxin, which is poisonous to insects and pests. So, this particular seed is basically systemically altered to include its own pesticide.

Initially, these GM 'Bt' plants seemed to resist pests and insects – allowing for larger yields but in the past few years, some pests have already become resistant to the plant. For the first time, in November 2009, Monsanto scientists were forced to admit that the Indian Bt cotton plant was no longer resistant to the pink bollworm pest.

Other seeds have been altered to include vitamins, like the Golden Rice seed which has 20 times more Beta-carotene than previous varieties.

Is it just plants or animals too?

Animals too have been genetically engineered to grow faster or produce more omega-3 fatty acids, for example. Check out Digital Journal for more info on GM salmon (www.digitaljournal.com/article/293934), which grows at twice the speed of a normal salmon, and a Science Daily story which takes a look at the effects of GM fish if they escape into the wild (www.sciencedaily.com/releases/2009/08/090827073250.htm).

What is the thinking behind GM?

There is much debate about how the world is going to feed itself, as our population increases. Scientists, researchers and environmentalists are split between believing that we need a scientific answer like GM in order to increase our food supply, while others believe there is no issue – beyond politics and logistics. Biotech companies claim GM offers a clean green future to help feed the world but environmentalists and other scientists completely disagree, claiming these companies are merely interested in their profits.

Why are they so controversial?

GM foods first came on the market in the early 1990s and have created controversy ever since. Pro-GM scientists see them as a way to feed the world, while other scientists and environmentalists cite possible safety issues, ecological and health concerns. But one of the most contentious issues is that of intellectual property. The GM companies that manufacture these seeds own the patents on these seeds.

And yet, for thousands of years, farmers have saved seeds to replant the following year. But if you're a farmer buying GM seeds from a biotech company, you're not legally allowed to save those seeds. In essence, the company still owns them. And the farmer is forced to buy them again, year in year, year out – or bear the brunt of the legal eagles who watch out for farmers in breach of their seed contract.

It is this point that environmentalists have a big problem with. They accuse biotech companies of wanting to own the world's seed supply. And they see GM as just the first step.

Who are these biotech companies?

Monsanto, Syngenta among others but by far the biggest player is Monsanto. Word has it they own 90% of the world's market in GM seeds and they also own one of the world's most popular herbicides – Round Up. So the same company that's selling the herbicide resistant seed, also owns the herbicide.

Monsanto writes…

'Growers who purchase our patented seeds sign a Monsanto Technology/Stewardship Agreement – an agreement that specifically addresses the obligations of both the grower and Monsanto and governs the use of the harvested crop. The agreement specifically states that the grower will not save or sell the seeds from their harvest for further planting, breeding or cultivation.'

Environmentalists and other critics accuse Monsanto of wanting to own the world's seed supply but Monsanto claims it's a clean, green biotech company that just wants to feed the world.

In an interview with Truthout, director of film *The World According to Monsanto* Marie Monique-Robin says…

'Nowadays Monsanto is the world leader in biotechnology and the first seed company. 90 per cent of the GMOs grown in the world belong to it. During the last decade, the firm bought dozens of seed companies all over the world, pushing its transgenic seeds, which are patented. A patented seed means that the farmers who grow it may not keep a part of their crops to re-sow it the next year, as farmers used to do everywhere in the world. In the US and Canada, farmers who grow transgenic crops must sign a 'technology agreement' – the no-sowing requirement is clearly expressed. If they don't respect the agreement and violate the patent, they are harassed by the 'gene police' and sued by Monsanto. Clearly, transgenic crops are just a tool to control the seed supply, which is the first link in the food chain, by forcing farmers to buy seeds each year.'

Don't GM seeds spread?

Like all seeds, GM seeds spread too, meaning that some farmers have discovered unwanted GM seeds contaminating their land – they are then, of course, forced to use them. In the US, many of those farmers have been investigated and prosecuted by Monsanto for patent theft – despite not being at all responsible for taking the seeds.

Has buying the seeds created problems for farmers?

Many farmers in India have also been forced to take out loans in order to pay for the new seeds.

What are the main issues for environmentalists?

According to the academic and environmentalist Dr Vandana Shiva, the biotech agenda for promoting GM is that the world will depend on them for every seed we plant and every crop we grow.

Although GM has been banned in the UK and Europe for the past 12 years, in recent months it looks as if the EFSA (European Food Standards Agency) has become more open to the idea, giving a GM potato and maize the green light to be grown and in July 2010, allowing member states to decide whether to accept or ban them. While in the UK, the *Daily Mail* reported finding illegal GM flax seeds in a loaf of M&S bread late in 2009.

2 July 2010

⇨ The above information is reprinted with kind permission from Debate Your Plate. Visit www.debateyourplate.com for more information on this and other related topics.

© *Debate Your Plate*

- WE'VE GENETICALLY MODIFIED FARMERS?!

- THEY DO EXACTLY AS WE SAY!!

MONSANTO

DEBATE YOUR PLATE

GM food Q&A

Genetically modified foods have polarised opinion in Britain since their creation, in some other countries they are widely accepted when a number of areas have imposed bans on their cultivation. Below are some of the issues about their use explained.

By Louise Gray, Environment Correspondent

Can we buy genetically modified crops on our supermarket shelves?

GM ingredients are already in food available on supermarket shelves, mostly in cooking oils containing GM soy or oilseed rape. However, these will be labelled, according to EU law. Most supermarkets have banned GM ingredients in their own-brand products. In the world as a whole we have eaten two trillion meals containing GM over the last 12 years.

Most farm animals in Britain are fed GM soy and no supermarket can guarantee that dairy or meat they stock is not from animals fed GM.

Is GM being grown in Britain?

The only GM crop licensed for growing on a commercial scale in Europe is unsuitable for UK conditions and is grown in northern Spain. However, other seeds are likely to come on the market soon. The most advanced GM crops that could be grown in Britain are GM potatoes and sugar beet, but these are yet to be licensed and commercial use is at least five years away. Scientists have been conducting two field trials under licence of GM crops in Norfolk and Yorkshire.

What are the benefits of GM crops?

Supporters say that we could develop crops that use less water and nutrients, are resistant to insects and produce higher yields. For western countries this could bring environmental benefits through lower pesticide use and water abstraction. In poorer countries it could help tackle starvation and improve the working conditions of farmers and labourers who would suffer less from pesticide contamination.

What are the disadvantages?

Opponents of GM say that the health effects are still unclear. They claim that sheep and goats are dying in India from eating genetically modified cotton. Critics reject claims of higher yields and say that the interests of big business are being put before health and environmental concerns. The potential for GM crops to contaminate organic farms, leading to loss of organic status, is also a huge worry.

What is the Government's position?

It says its policy towards GM is 'precautionary, evidence-based and sensitive to public concerns'.

It describes the technology as 'not wholly good or bad' and promises to consider GM crops on a case by case basis, with the public the ultimate arbiters of whether GM products should succeed.

However, in recent years the position has been warming, as the public attitude softens towards GM and scientists call for a more open attitude to GM because of food shortages in other parts of the world and the need to grow crops in dry or difficult areas.

Ultimately the EU has the power to approve or reject GM crops and Brussels has also been softening its position as the rest of the world, particularly South America, embraces the new technology.

Every year more than 300 million acres of GM are planted around the world.

24 January 2011

Production of GM foods

GM, or genetically modified, food involves altering a plant, animal or micro-organism's genes or inserting one from another organism – that is, a living thing. Genes carry the instructions for all the characteristics that an organism inherits. They are made up of DNA.

Sometimes the term 'biotechnology' is used to describe genetic modification. This also has a wider meaning of using micro-organisms or biological techniques to process waste or produce useful compounds, such as vaccines.

How it's being used

People have been breeding animals and new varieties of plants for many hundreds of years to develop or avoid certain qualities. Examples include racehorses that are bred to be faster and stronger, and roses, bred to give a wider range of colours and to make them more resistant to disease. Over many generations, sometimes for thousands of years, the world's main food crops have been selected, crossed and bred to suit the conditions they are grown in and to make them tastier.

For example, cattle are bred according to whether they are for beef or dairy herds. Most of today's dairy cattle are very different from the cattle that were originally domesticated. Over the years, dairy herd breeding has focused on increasing milk yield and on improving the quality of the milk.

But whereas traditional methods involve mixing thousands of genes, genetic modification allows just one individual gene, or a small number of genes, to be inserted into a plant, animal or micro-organism (such as bacteria), to change it in a pre-determined way. Through genetic modification, genes can also be 'switched' on or off to change the way a plant or animal develops.

For example, herbicides are used to kill weeds in fields of crops but they can also affect the growth of the crops they are intended to protect. By using genetic modification, a gene with a particular characteristic, such as resistance to a specific herbicide, can be introduced into a crop plant. When that herbicide is sprayed on the field to kill the weeds, it will not hinder the growth of the crops.

Similarly, genetic modification can be used to reduce the amount of pesticide needed by altering a plant's DNA so it can resist the particular insect pests that attack it. Genetic modification can also be used to give crops immunity to plant viruses or to improve the nutritional value of a plant. In animals intended for food, genetic modification could potentially increase how fast and to what size they grow.

Genetic modification allows plants, animals and micro-organisms to be produced with specific qualities more accurately and efficiently than through traditional methods. It also allows genes to be transferred from one species to another to develop characteristics that would be very difficult or impossible to achieve through traditional breeding. For example, genes can be introduced from one plant to another plant, from a plant to an animal, or from an animal to a plant. Transferring genes between plants and animals is a particular area of debate.

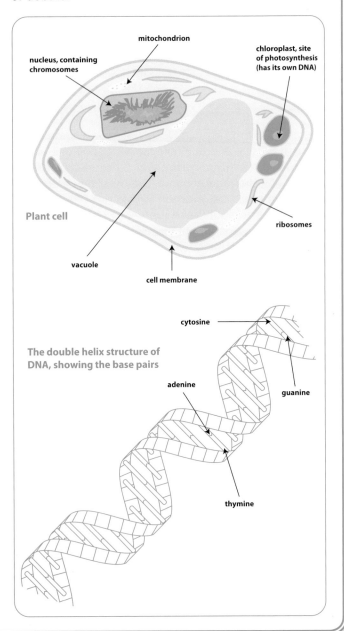

Plant cell

nucleus, containing chromosomes

mitochondrion

chloroplast, site of photosynthesis (has its own DNA)

vacuole

cell membrane

ribosomes

The double helix structure of DNA, showing the base pairs

cytosine

adenine

guanine

thymine

What is DNA?

DNA stands for deoxyribonucleic acid. It is the genetic material contained in the cells of all living things and it carries the information that allows organisms to function, repair and reproduce themselves.

Every cell of plants (see diagram opposite), micro-organisms (such as bacteria), animals, and people contain many thousands of different genes, which are made of DNA. These genes determine the characteristics, or genetic make-up, of every living thing, including the food we eat. When we eat any food, we are eating the genes and breaking down the DNA present in the food.

DNA is made up of two separate strands of what are called 'nucleotides'. These are the building blocks of DNA and are twisted around each other in a double helix structure (see diagram opposite). The identity of a gene and the function it performs are determined by the number of nucleotides and the particular order in which they are strung together on chromosomes – this is known as the 'sequence' of the gene. Chromosomes are the cell structures that carry the DNA.

How are GM foods assessed for safety?

Any GM foods intended for sale in the European Union are subject to a rigorous safety assessment, which is the responsibility of the European Food Safety Authority (EFSA).

However, the final decision for authorisation still rests with Member States, which vote on each GM food. In the event of an inconclusive vote, the Council of Ministers votes, and if they cannot agree the final decision rests with the European Commission.

EFSA is responsible for publishing information concerning applications submitted under this legislation. Further details can be found on the EFSA website.

The Food Standards Agency is the UK authority named in the European legislation, and is advised on both GM and novel foods by an independent body of experts called the Advisory Committee on Novel Foods and Processes (ACNFP) and on GM animal feed by the Advisory Committee on Animal Feedingstuffs (ACAF). The ACNFP is responsible for assessing the safety of novel and GM food, and ACAF is responsible for assessing the safety of GM feed.

The Board of the Food Standards Agency stated in June 2000 that it was satisfied that the safety assessment procedures for GM foods were sufficiently robust and rigorous to ensure that approved GM foods were as safe as their non-GM counterparts, and posed no additional risk to the consumer.

Each GM food is assessed for safety, including its toxicological, nutritional and allergenic potential, on a case-by-case basis before it can be approved for marketing.

The Agency supports consumer choice. We recognise that some people will want to choose not to buy or eat genetically modified (GM) foods, however carefully they have been assessed for safety.

In 2003, the Agency supported a range of initiatives to independently assess public opinion on the acceptability of GM food and how this relates to consumer choice. This formed the Agency's contribution to the Government's public debate on GM. Details of the various activities we supported can be found on our GM food debate website and were summarised in our submission to the Government's GM public debate.

How is GM used in food production?

Genetic modification can be used in a number of ways in food production. These range from modifying the raw ingredients to using genetic modification during processing.

When genetic modification is used as a part of the production process, as described in 4 below, the GM material does not end up in the food on our plates. This is similar to other processing techniques, so, for example, when a food processor is used for slicing, no part of the processor ends up in the meal we eat.

These are the different ways that genetic modification can be used in food production:

1 GM food: A crop, such as a fruit or vegetable, or an animal can be genetically modified. (However, no animal or human genes, or GM animals, have been approved for use in GM food in the EU.)

2 GM ingredients: Food that comes from a GM crop, such as maize, can be processed, for example into flour, and the GM DNA is still present in the food and can be identified.

3 'GM-derived' ingredients: Food can come from a GM crop but the DNA can be processed out of the final product – this is called 'GM-derived'. An example of this is soy oil, which is made from GM soya beans. The processing breaks up the DNA so that it can no longer be identified either as GM DNA or conventional DNA in the final oil because it has been broken down into small fragments containing nucleotides – these are DNA building blocks. Therefore, soy oil from GM soya beans cannot be distinguished from soy oil from conventional beans.

4 GM processing aid: A GM organism can also be used to make a product without GM material being present in the ingredients or in the final product. In this case

the GM organism is a 'processing aid'. One example is hard cheese production. The enzyme chymosin is the active ingredient of rennet, which is used to curdle milk. Traditionally, rennet has been taken from calves' stomachs, but the demand for cheese is greater than the number of calves available and the chymosin does not always produce consistent batches of cheese. Today, the gene responsible for producing chymosin is inserted in bacteria, so the bacteria make the chymosin instead of using traditional rennet. Only the bacteria are genetically modified, not the chymosin, and so the cheese has no GM content because the bacteria are not part of the cheese.

5   GM ingredients in animal feed: GM crops, such as maize, are also used to feed animals that are later eaten, such as chickens. There are also animal products, such as eggs and milk, which come from animals fed on GM crops. Functioning GM DNA is not, however, in the meat that we eat or these animal products. See the following two paragraphs that explain what happens to DNA in our bodies and during food processing.

How does processing affect the DNA in foods?

DNA is broken up in the same way that food processing can alter or destroy other characteristics of food ingredients, such as texture, during manufacturing. Processing includes all the stages involved in getting food ready for us to eat, from refining raw materials to cooking in our homes.

What happens when people eat GM food?

Human beings have always eaten plants and animals, which means we have always eaten their DNA without it causing any health problems. Given that GM DNA is still DNA, eating it should not pose any greater risk than eating non-GM DNA. Indeed, no one has ever been reported as suffering from illness because the food they had eaten had been genetically modified.

When someone eats GM food it is processed in the same way as non-GM food. When we eat any food, our digestive systems break down the tissue, the proteins, and the DNA in the food. The DNA in GM food has the same structure as non-GM DNA and is broken down in the same way. Most DNA that is consumed, whether GM or not, is broken down in our stomachs and intestines.

Sometimes, the DNA from the food we eat isn't broken down. However, it is unlikely that this DNA will become part of our genetic material by passing into our cells – any non-human DNA should simply be broken down in the cell.

Will the label tell me if the food is GM?

The Agency supports consumer choice. We recognise that some people will want to choose not to buy or eat GM foods, however carefully they have been assessed for safety.

In the EU, if a food contains or consists of genetically modified organisms (GMOs), or contains ingredients produced from GMOs, this must be indicated on the label. For GM products sold 'loose', information must be displayed immediately next to the food to indicate that it is GM.

On 18 April 2004, new rules for GM labelling came into force in all EU Member States. These cover all GM food and animal feed, regardless of the presence of any GM material in the final product.

This means products such as flour, oils and glucose syrups have to be labelled as GM if they are from a GM source. Products produced with GM technology (cheese produced with GM enzymes, for example) do not have to be labelled.

Products such as meat, milk and eggs from animals fed on GM animal feed also don't need labelling.

Any intentional use of GM ingredients at any level must be labelled. But there is no need to label small amounts of approved GM ingredients (below 0.9% for approved GM varieties) that are accidentally present in a food.

⇨ The above information is reprinted with kind permission from the Food Standards Agency. Visit www.food.gov.uk for more information.

© Crown copyright

- IT'S ALL DNA, YOU CAN'T TASTE THE DIFFERENCE...

- YOU, HAVEN'T TRIED BROCCOLI...

GM crops ten years on: hope, hype and reality

The divisive debate about GM rages on, but how has this controversial technology served us in the last ten years?

By Ian Scoones, co-director ESRC STEPS Centre

A decade ago there was much hope and hype about the potential of GM crops. They were going to feed the world and solve poverty and development issues. It was claimed that pest-resistant crops using so-called Bt technologies to resist insect predation could reduce pesticide use and improve farmers' incomes, and that technologies for dealing with drought or nutrient deficits were in the pipeline. GM crops would help poorer farmers in the developing world, with a 'gene revolution' succeeding the 'green revolution' of previous decades.

However, others predicted disaster: GM crops would result in environmental and health catastrophes and global domination of agriculture by large corporations. Just as the pro-GM lobby could be accused of excessive, unfounded hype, anti-GM campaigners often generated doomsday scenarios based on limited evidence.

> **About 98 million hectares out of a global GM crop area of 125 million hectares were grown in just three countries, by large-scale farmers: the United States (62.5 million), Argentina (21 million) and Brazil (15 million)**

In reality, a more complex and mixed story has emerged. In some circumstances, some farmers have benefited from GM crop technologies while others had bad experiences or were bypassed altogether. But even now, wild claims are still made and false expectations generated.

GM crops have expanded rapidly in some locations. Annual assessments by Clive James of ISAAA, the International Service for the Acquisition of Agri-biotech Applications, show GM crops sweeping the globe selectively. GM crops were planted in 25 countries in 2008, but only eight countries planted more than a million hectares.

About 98 million hectares out of a global GM crop area of 125 million hectares were grown in just three countries, by large-scale farmers: the United States (62.5 million), Argentina (21 million) and Brazil (15 million). The GM crops which have been commercialised are primarily insect-resistant Bt maize and cotton, and herbicide-tolerant soy.

A recent book by Robert Paarlberg, *Starved For Science: How Biotechnology Is Being Kept Out Of Africa*, again makes the case for GM crops as a solution to agricultural development.

> **Biotechnology companies are accountable to their shareholders, not the rural poor of the global south**

Paarlberg argues that Africa's poor have scandalously been denied the vital, life-saving technology of GM crops because of European anti-GM campaigns. He claims that inappropriate, precautionary biosafety regulation is a major hurdle to the widespread adoption of poverty-reducing technologies.

Paarlberg's arguments have been picked up by policymakers and lobby groups, the latter arguing the 'tide is turning' in favour of GM crops as a result of the political recognition of the global food crisis. New efforts are making the case for a GM solution, especially for the potentially vast markets of the developing world, for example through the industry-based Alliance for Abundant Food and Energy.

A complex story with mixed impacts

Dominic Glover's research at the ESRC Social Technological and Environmental Pathways to Sustainability (STEPS) Centre reveals a complex story with mixed impacts. Glover shows that economic returns are highly variable. GM crops only perform well in good varieties, GM seed start-up costs and technology fees are sometimes too expensive for poorer farmers, and major adopters are usually richer, with more land. Meanwhile, the institutional and policy environment is vital: without support, credit and sustained backing, new technologies often fail.

Lessons for the future

The 'pro-' versus 'anti-' fundamentalists of the GM debate have become entrenched. How do we get beyond this stalemate? STEPS Centre research suggests five ways:

⇨ GM is not the only biotech solution on offer. Marker-assisted selection and other genomic techniques offer could enhance conventional breeding through

ECONOMIC AND SOCIAL RESEARCH COUNCIL

biotechnology. Investment in long-term, local, context-specific breeding and crop development programmes is needed.

⇨ Technologies are never isolated from social, economic, political contexts. The many ways in which farmers manage plants, their soils and the wider environment matter.

⇨ Biotechnology companies are accountable to their shareholders, not the rural poor of the global south. Their business models are focused on widespread adoption of standardised technologies on large farms.

⇨ The ownership of technologies, and the control of their development, matter. Involving farmers in priority-setting and upstream technology design is vital. Users of technology understand their own problems best.

⇨ In the face of deep uncertainty, a precautionary stance makes for sound policy. Appropriate regulatory infrastructure is a developing world challenge – each context requires particular regulatory and policy responses based on local evidence. Making technologies work for the poor is inevitably a 'slow race', resulting in more robust and effective governance.

From the ESRC magazine Britain in 2011
26 January 2011

⇨ The above information is reprinted with kind permission from the Economic and Social Research Council. Visit www.esrc.ac.uk for more information on this and other related topics.

© *Economic and Social Research Council (ESRC)*

GM crops flourishing in developing world, says report

Information from SciDev.net.

By Chen Weixiao

The planting of genetically modified crops has surged, particularly in developing countries, because of the global food crisis, according to a report.

The number of countries growing GM crops has increased from six in 1996, the first year of commercialisation, to 25 in 2009, says the latest annual report of the International Service for the Acquisition of Agri-biotech Application (ISAAA), released in Beijing last month (23 February).

Around 134 million hectares worldwide are now planted with GM crops.

The United States tops the list of countries growing GM crops, followed by Brazil, Argentina, India, Canada, China, Paraguay and South Africa. Almost half of global GM crops are now planted in 16 developing countries, involving 13 million small farmers. ISAAA predicts that the number of biotech farmers will reach 20 million or more by 2015.

'This strong adoption puts to rest the idea that [GM] crops can only benefit larger farmers and industrialised countries,' said Huang Dafang, a researcher at the Chinese Academy of Agricultural Sciences' Biotechnology Research Institute.

Burkina Faso's GM cotton area increased from 8,500 hectares to 115,000 hectares – almost a third of the country's total cotton area – from 1996 to 2009.

'It is unwise to say no to GM technology considering the food crisis the world faces,' Clive James, chair of ISAAA, told SciDev.Net.

'The most promising technological strategy at this time for increasing global food, feed and fibre productivity is to combine the best of the old and the best of the new, by integrating the best of conventional crop technology and the best of crop biotechnology applications including novel traits,' he said.

But non-governmental organisation Friends of the Earth questioned whether GM crops have been as successful as ISAAA portrays.

In a report released on the same day, it said that GM crops occupy less than three per cent of global agricultural land and that more than 99 per cent of the crops are grown for animal feed and agrofuels rather than food.

'There is still not a single commercial GM crop with increased yield, drought-tolerance, salt-tolerance, enhanced nutrition or other beneficial traits long promised by biotech companies,' said the report, pointing out that '99 per cent of biotech agriculture consists of four crops with just two traits, herbicide-tolerance and/or insect-resistance'.

It said that India has placed a moratorium on the planting of its first GM food crop due to widespread concerns on its health, environmental and socio-economic impact.

8 March 2010

⇨ The above information is reprinted with kind permission from SciDev.net.

© *SciDev.net*

EC approves first GM crop in a decade

From the Royal Society of Chemistry's magazine Chemistry World.

By Ned Stafford

The European Commission has authorised cultivation of a new GM crop for the first time in 12 years, approving BASF's genetically modified potato Amflora for industrial use. The move has given GM advocates hope that a backlog of applications for other GM crops will also be authorised.

In addition to giving German chemical giant BASF its long-sought approval for Amflora, genetically modified to produce pure amylopectin starch for technical applications in the paper, textile and adhesives industries, the commission on 2 March issued a complementary authorisation covering use of the potato's starch by-products as feed. The commission also announced authorisations for three GM maize products – from Monsanto, Syngenta and Pioneer – to be placed on the market for food and feed uses but not for cultivation.

Morten Nielsen, director of green biotechnology at the European Association for Bioindustries (EuropaBio), described the authorisations as the EU's return to 'sound policy' on GM issues, adding that the decisions were made on the basis of stringent regulatory rules and scientific risk assessment.

'I think this is a very positive first step in the right direction,' he says. But noting that an additional 17 GM products for cultivation are still tied up in the 'approval process' along with 44 products for food and feed, import and processing in the EU, he added: 'we still have a way to go'.

Stefan Marcinowski, BASF executive board member, echoes Nielsen's sentiments: 'after waiting for more than 13 years, we are delighted that the European Commission has approved Amflora,' he says. 'We hope that this decision is a milestone for further innovative products that will promote competitive and sustainable agriculture in Europe.'

BASF will begin commercial cultivation of Amflora this year, with crops planned for sites in Germany, the Czech Republic, Sweden and the Netherlands.

While the news was welcomed by the biotechnology sector, GM opponents have been critical of the decision, saying the procedure used to approve Amflora removed the opportunity for public debate.

They contend that Amflora contains a gene resistant to certain antibiotics that could raise bacterial resistance to drugs when released into the environment.

The Commission's health and consumer policy commissioner, John Dalli, emphasised that the decisions announced on 2 March were made following years of favourable safety assessments by the European Food Safety Authority. 'It became clear to me that there were no new scientific issues that merited further assessment,' he said. 'All scientific issues, particularly those concerning safety, had been fully addressed. Any delay would have simply been unjustified.'

Alongside the authorisations, the European Commission also announced plans to complete a proposal by the summer on how it will combine a central European authorisation system with freedom for member states to decide whether to cultivate GM crops on their territory.

⇨ Reproduced by permission of the Royal Society of Chemistry from Ned Stafford, *Chemistry World*, 2 March 2010 (http://www.rsc.org/chemistryworld/News/2010/March/05031001.asp).

ROYAL SOCIETY OF CHEMISTRY

EU angers all camps with move to relax GM crop restrictions

European Commission proposals manage to infuriate both pro- and anti-GM lobby groups.

By BusinessGreen.com staff

The use of genetically modified (GM) crops in the EU could become more common over the next decade, after the European Commission yesterday unveiled plans that would give individual member states the freedom to decide whether or not to permit the production of GM crops.

However, both pro- and anti-GM lobby groups have expressed frustration at the new proposals, warning that they could create a patchwork of regulations across the EU where some states allow GM crops and others maintain a blanket ban on all GM produce.

The proposals, which still have to be approved by the European Parliament and council of member states, are designed to end a decade-long deadlock that has seen EU attempts to approve certain GM crops for use repeatedly blocked by countries opposed to the use of GM.

Under the proposals, individual member states will be able to choose to restrict or ban the use of GM crops on non-scientific grounds such as socio-economic or cultural reasons.

'The concrete measures adopted today will allow member states the freedom to decide on GMO (genetically modified organism) cultivation,' said health and consumer policy commissioner John Dalli. 'Experience with GMOs so far shows that member states need more flexibility to organise the co-existence of GM and other types of crops such as conventional and organic crops.'

In return for handing powers back to member states, the EU is hoping that countries opposed to GM will stop blocking its efforts to certify certain GM crops as safe. Countries that have been pushing to expand the use of GM crops, such as Spain and the Netherlands, would then be free to begin commercial production of approved crops.

However, while broadly supportive of moves that should allow the EU to move towards certifying certain GM crops for use, experts in the agricultural industry voiced fears that farmers operating in EU countries where GM crops are banned could be forced to operate at a competitive disadvantage to rivals in neighbouring countries where GM crops are permitted.

Meanwhile, anti-GM groups slammed the decision, warning that the move would open the door for the wider use of GM crops that they regard as potentially harmful.

> **[The new proposals] could create a patchwork of regulations across the EU where some states allow GM crops and others maintain a blanket ban on all GM produce**

'While the European Commission is seemingly offering countries the right to implement national bans, in reality the proposal aims to do the opposite – opening Europe's fields to GM crops,' said Friends of the Earth Europe's food campaigner Mute Schimpf. 'The Commission continues to fail to protect Europe's food and feed from contamination by GM crops, and we urge countries to reject this deal as it stands.'

14 July 2010

⇨ The above information is reprinted with kind permission from BusinessGreen. Visit www.businessgreen.com for more information.

© BusinessGreen

Animal genetics and biotechnology

Biotechnology may be defined as 'the application of our advancing understanding of living organisms and their components to create industrial products and processes'.

All animal breeding, either from farm livestock such as dairy or beef cattle, or for companion animals such as the many different breeds of dogs, is a type of biotechnology that has been going on for many centuries. Breeders have selected animals that show particular characteristics or traits and used them in breeding programmes to ensure that these traits are retained. What they have been doing is selecting animals with particular combinations of genes. We now know that this type of conventional breeding of animals involves hundreds of genes, most of which are unidentified.

Mapping genes

Modern molecular biology is making it possible to identify how different genes control different characteristics. Scientists are 'mapping' the genes on the chromosomes, so that they can see where genes are located and how they function within cells and processes within the animal. This will help identify which combinations give the traits that are desired, making selection of animals carrying the best of the naturally occurring genetic variation more effective. Some traits are determined by a single gene and these are relatively easy to study. But others, including commercially important traits such as growth rate and feed conversion efficiency, are controlled by many genes working together. One important research goal is to find genes that make animals resistant to diseases. Selecting for these genes will help produce naturally healthier animals and reduce farmers' reliance on antibiotics and other veterinary drugs. In addition, knowing the processes that contribute to health and disease in animals will help us understand the function of the very similar systems that affect human health.

The full sequence of all genes (the genome sequence) has recently been derived for chickens and cattle and will soon be available for pigs. These sequences allow us to identify the similarities and differences between different livestock species and between livestock and humans. This sequence greatly aids our ability to identify important genes and understand the causes of healthy development or disease susceptibility.

Genetic modification

The traditional selection and mapping described above makes use of naturally occurring gene variants. However, there are a number of reasons why it might be valuable to alter existing gene variants or add new genes. As well as identifying and isolating individual genes, molecular biology enables scientists to transfer these genes from one individual to another – so called genetic modification or transgenics. This could further accelerate livestock improvement but its usefulness in the foreseeable future is most likely in the area of obtaining high-value medical products from animals rather than in agriculture.

Why are scientists researching the uses of transgenic animals?

There are five main areas in which the production of transgenic animals offer potential benefits.

⇨ To produce therapeutics for human medicine – In 2006 the European Medicines Agency approved the use of a therapeutic used to prevent blood clotting that is produced in goats' milk. Recently, scientists have bred several generations of transgenic chickens that produce therapeutics in the egg white. This offers the potential for producing high-value therapeutics in the eggs of genetically modified chickens.

⇨ To provide models of human disease – The function and control of genes implicated in human disease can be studied in animals.

⇨ To provide tissue for use in human transplant surgery – The recognition molecules on animal cells may be tailored so that they are no longer rejected as foreign by humans.

⇨ To improve the efficiency of livestock breeding and to increase the range and quality of livestock products.

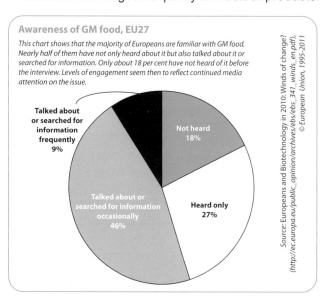

Awareness of GM food, EU27

This chart shows that the majority of Europeans are familiar with GM food. Nearly half of them have not only heard about it but also talked about it or searched for information. Only about 18 per cent have not heard of it before the interview. Levels of engagement seem then to reflect continued media attention on the issue.

Talked about or searched for information frequently 9%

Not heard 18%

Talked about or searched for information occasionally 46%

Heard only 27%

Source: Europeans and Biotechnology in 2010: Winds of change? (http://ec.europa.eu/public_opinion/archives/ebs/ebs_341_winds_en.pdf), © European Union, 1995-2011

FARMING AND COUNTRYSIDE EDUCATION

⇨ More speculatively, to improve animal health – Long term it should be possible to identify genes that confer resistance to disease and to introduce these into livestock, so reducing reliance on antibiotics and chemicals to control disease.

How genes are introduced into animal cells

Newly fertilised egg cells contain two pronuclei (one originating from the egg cell and one from the sperm) each of which carries half the full complement of chromosomes. The pronuclei fuse to form the nucleus of the fertilised cell which then divides to form the embryo. Newly fertilised cells can be isolated and immobilised under a microscope. A very fine glass needle is used to inject DNA directly into one of the pronuclei. The egg is then transferred into a foster mother where it grows and divides normally to produce the embryo. A new technique called nuclear transfer enables scientists to remove the nucleus from an egg cell and replace it with a nucleus from another cell. In this way the complete genetic information of the donor cell is incorporated into the recipient. The cells may be genetically modified in the lab before they are transferred to the recipient.

⇨ The above information is reprinted with kind permission from Farming and Countryside Education (FACE). Visit http://face-online.org.uk for more.

© Farming and Countryside Education

GM chickens breakthrough to prevent spread of bird flu

Information from the BBSRC.

Researchers funded by BBSRC have developed chickens that are genetically modified to prevent them from spreading bird flu to other chickens. If this genetic modification is introduced into poultry flocks in the future it has the potential to protect the health of the birds and so increase the production of meat and eggs. It could also reduce the risk of bird flu epidemics that can lead to new flu outbreaks in the human population.

The study, which the researchers say is the first step in developing chickens that are completely resistant to avian flu, was published last night in the journal *Science*. The work was carried out by teams based in The Roslin Institute, an institute of BBSRC, at the University of Edinburgh and in the University of Cambridge Department of Veterinary Medicine.

Professor Helen Sang, who led the team at The Roslin Institute, said that as well as improving welfare and sustainability in the poultry industry, 'this work could also form the basis for improving economic and food security in many regions of the world where bird flu is a significant problem'.

Meat production and consumption worldwide is increasing in general and poultry makes up a significant proportion of that increase. There appears to be a trend towards eating chicken as a major source of protein and as the global population is predicted to hit nine billion in 2050, 'infectious diseases of livestock represent a significant threat to global food security', says Professor Douglas Kell, BBSRC Chief Executive.

There is also the potential, Professor Kell added, for infectious diseases of livestock to 'jump to humans and become pandemic'. This, he says, 'has been identified by the Government as a top-level national security risk'.

Dr Laurence Tiley, Senior Lecturer in Virology who led the team that developed the inhibitory transgene at the University of Cambridge, said: 'Chickens are potential bridging hosts that can enable new strains of flu to be transmitted to humans. Preventing virus transmission in chickens should reduce the risk posed to people exposed to infected birds.'

To produce these chickens, the scientists introduced a new gene that manufactures a small 'decoy' molecule. In this case, it is a short length of a type of molecule called ribonucleic acid, or RNA. Dr Tiley explained that 'the decoy mimics an essential part of the flu virus genome that is identical for all strains of influenza A. The replication machinery of the virus is tricked into recognising the decoy molecule instead of the viral genome and this interferes with the replication cycle of the virus'.

The decoy is expected to work against all strains of bird flu and will not need updating for each season.

'The virus will find it difficult to evolve to escape the effects of the decoy. This is quite different from conventional flu vaccines, which need to be updated in the face of virus evolution as they tend only to protect against closely matching strains of virus and do not always prevent spread within a flock,' Dr Tiley concluded.

14 January 2011

⇨ The above information is reprinted with kind permission from the BBSRC. Visit www.bbsrc.ac.uk for more information.

© BBSRC

Is nanotechnology the new GM?

Engineered nanoparticles are very similar to genetically modified organisms in terms of the issues they raise around democratic control of the development of potentially risky technologies. Jo Southall investigates.

Democratic deficit?

The Soil Association, which refuses to give its Organic label to products containing nanomaterials, summed up some of the key issues around nanotechnology in 2008:

⇨ Commercial opportunities have run ahead of scientific understanding and regulatory control.

⇨ The industry is trying to win over Government backing with compelling claims about the benefits of the technology and to win over consumers by promoting individual products, whilst neglecting the fundamental issues of safety.

⇨ Initial studies show some negative effects and there is a list of potential health impacts that have yet to be investigated by scientists.

⇨ Regulators have not reacted to the scientific evidence of health effects for products that are already commercialised, instead accepting industry reassurances and unpublished industry evidence.

⇨ The standard of proof is being set very high for any concerns, but low for reasons to dismiss concerns and without the context of a body of established scientific knowledge to judge conflicting arguments.

⇨ Concerns are being downplayed on the basis of absence of any consensus over health problems and with arguments that some nanoparticles occur in nature or have been produced by industry for some time.

There are a range of other concerns commonly highlighted by campaigners which can be summarised as follows:

⇨ Big business and to some extent governments are controlling the development of nanotechnologies without a mandate from the public.

⇨ The possible impacts of nanotechnologies on the most vulnerable are not being taken into account.

⇨ Many of the applications of these technologies are seeking to solve either problems that aren't really problems (e.g. reducing wrinkles), or problems that already have much more sustainable solutions, such as obesity. The Government's own report into obesity, for example, highlighted the lack of access to fresh fruit and vegetables and exercising opportunities. But for some the ease of tackling the problem through a technofix is seen as preferable to addressing access issues. Addressing obesity in a sustainable way could lead to the creation of more 'social capital' by, for example, people exercising together and shopping more locally.

The applications

In our report on sunscreens, we look in detail at the growing use of nanotechnologies in sun protection. And even our report on fridges mentions in passing one or two fridges now using nanoparticles. This is because there has been an explosion in the use of nanotechnologies in the last few years in both consumer and non-consumer products. Toothpaste, cosmetics, sunscreen, diamonds, clothing, cooking oil and car accessories are just some of the new nanotechnology consumer products on the shelves in the US.

According to an inventory collated by the US Project on Emerging Nanotechnologies (PEN), new products are now appearing at a rate of three to four a week. PEN's database (www.nanotechproject.org/inventories) lists more than 800 products, from luggage to construction materials, and from bicycles to children's goods.

Nanoparticles also have medical applications, which you could come into contact with when receiving treatment. One of the consumer applications that causes most concern is nanofoods. A recent 'Nanofoods' documentary stated that the Foods Standards Agency are trying to make UK regulations clearer than those in the US, where nanofoods are on sale due to a loophole (they are also on sale in China, Australia and Israel). Nanofoods are currently unauthorised in the UK, but there is an ongoing House of Lords enquiry into nanofoods and food packaging.

In March this year, EU members voted for a *de facto* moratorium on nanofood. Nanotechnologies also have military applications said to be more potentially significant than nuclear weapons. In February 2009, questions were asked about these applications in the European Parliament. For more information about nanotech and the military see the 2006 book *Military Nanotechnology: Potential Applications And Preventive Arms Control* by Jurgen Altmann.

The lack of public debate and transparency

Since *Ethical Consumer* last looked at nanotechnology (in issue 93 in 2005), the number of projects have expanded

considerably. Go to the nanowerk.com website and you'll find a calendar with a nano seminar or conference on almost every day of the year, with titles from NanoAfrica to NanoCancer. And for some time now, nanotechnologies have also been converging with other areas of science giving us a range of new and unfamiliar terms such as nanobiotechnology, synthetic biology, DNA computing and neuroengineering.

What hasn't expanded much is transparency. In 2006 the UK Government started a two-year project involving a voluntary register of 'engineered nanoscale materials'. The register was not in the public domain and received only 12 responses.

The Government also has a Nanotechnologies Stakeholder Forum and has spent an average of £600,000 per year over the last five years to research the toxicology, environmental and health impacts of nano-materials. This has to be seen in the context of the £90 million that the Government spent in 2004 alone on other nanoscience research and commercial promotion.

There is no current law in Europe requiring products containing nanomaterials to be labelled as such. In the UK only items with the Soil Association label and all other food items can be said to be free from engineered nanoparticles. Products listed on the PEN database are only nanotechnology-based. For everything else consumers have to rely on the company to voluntarily disclose this information – as some of the better sunscreen companies like Green People have done.

Campaigning on nanotech

Environmental NGOs often play a key part in stimulating public debate in the UK around technology, but on nanotech there's almost an eerie silence, due possibly to the need to focus resources on the more urgent issue of climate change. In November 2008, Which? press released a report into nanoparticles in cosmetics. Which? called for a range of measures, including clear consumer information about nanomaterials in cosmetics and mandatory reporting by companies of their use of manufactured nanomaterials. The report also included a call for an internationally-agreed definition and that the Precautionary Principle be 'applied to products where there are potential risks, but where it is not currently possible to assess their safety' and for the Government/ EU to fund further research and for clear regulation.

Other NGOs are calling for a range of measures. ETC Group – a Canadian technology campaign organisation – want a moratorium on the development, release and commercialisation of nanomaterials and nanobiotech, pending inclusive global societal dialogue and stronger oversight of emerging technologies. Friends of the Earth Europe are in accord with the Which? and ETC Group demands, but in addition are calling for a moratorium on

the use of nanotech applications, and for all who market nano products, or sell nano-containing products to the public to be held accountable for liabilities incurred by their products.

For some the debate is complicated by the good uses of nanotechnologies, including some solar panels and emissions control systems that are already on the market, drug delivery systems that are already in use, and numerous other applications that are in use or development.

Risks and toxicity

Engineered nanoparticles exist in 'free' applications, such as skin creams, and 'fixed' applications like bicycle frames. In theory, fixed applications pose fewer risks, but this assumes safe disposal methods and no breakage. There are also concerns around bioaccumulation.

In addition, sometimes the distinction between free and fixed is unclear. For example, there is already evidence of nanoparticles in socks being released into the water supply.

The commercial rewards for being first to develop a new technology can be so substantial that they can be seen to encourage the cutting of corners. According to Jim Thomas of ETC Group, the European Commission has a view that the toxicology of genetically modified organisms (GMOs) can be assessed, but has a provisional view that the toxicology of nanomaterials cannot be assessed using traditional methods.

This provisional view is based on the work of the highest EU body on toxicology, which spent a year researching whether existing toxicology methods were appropriate for assessing nanomaterials. Their answer was basically 'no', but what little toxicology there already is on the subject tells us that 'there is already much more evidence for the toxicity of nanoparticles than, for example, GMOs which have been under scrutiny far longer (although toxicity varies from nanoparticle to nanoparticle, as it does from GMO to GMO)'.

What's often forgotten about in discussion on the safety of nanoparticles is that, if and when sufficient toxicology exists, it's more than likely that animal testing will form a large part of testing regimes. Indeed it's already the case that one of the most quoted pieces of research on nanotoxicity involved tests on mice. For these reasons, the Dr Hadwen Trust is calling for the making of nanoparticles for non-essential, non-medical use to be banned, for their use in medical applications to be judged on a case-by-case basis and for no testing on sentient animals.

⇨ The above information is reprinted with kind permission from Ethical Consumer. Visit www.ethicalconsumer.org for more information or to view references for this article.

© *Ethical Consumer*

Chapter 2

THE DEBATE

The GM debate in context

Is it time for the UK to embrace the commercial planting of GM crops?

By Helen Birtwistle

What's new about GM technology?

For thousands of years farmers and plant breeders have been changing the genetic makeup of crops to improve characteristics like size, resistance to disease and taste. They started simply by sowing only those seeds that came from plants with desirable traits. Later, knowledge about plant reproduction enabled crossbreeding of plants to create new crops, with scientists using chemicals and radiation to introduce favourable mutations. Now genetic engineering makes it possible to overcome natural reproductive barriers, as a single gene with a desired function can be transferred into an existing crop variety. At the centre of the debate is the question of whether GM is simply the next stage in the development of agricultural technologies or whether it represents a new departure with risky and irreversible consequences.

Because genetic modification is more precise than crossbreeding it involves the transfer of less genetic material and is said to be more predictable

Does GM create new risks?

Plant scientists generally claim the former. Because genetic modification is more precise than crossbreeding it involves the transfer of less genetic material and is said to be more predictable [Ref: BBC News]. However, environmentalists have expressed concern about the introduction of genes not previously found in the food supply, like a human liver gene inserted into rice to allow it to break down herbicides and pollutants. They argue that the transfer of genes is a haphazard process, breaking up the natural sequencing of genes and leading to unforeseen consequences [Ref: Independent]. In response, it has been argued that these risks must be put into context. Non-GM agriculture is not risk free and we accept some risks from foods like peanuts which

were not tested when first sold in this country but are now known to cause severe allergic reactions. There is also some evidence that GM could damage farmland biodiversity, which environmentalists argue should signal the end of GM in the UK [Ref: BBC News]. But supporters of GM say that threats to biodiversity are exaggerated. Changing farming practices will create winners and losers, but the impact on wildlife will not be uniformly negative.

What does food biotechnology have to offer?

Critics complain that most GM technologies focus on developing characteristics valuable to rich farmers, such as herbicide and insect resistance [Ref: *Independent*]. However, concerns about food security have given a new urgency to research priorities. China announced the launch of a new research centre to develop high-yield and pest-resistant GM crops [Ref: RSC]. Meanwhile, a former UK Government Chief Scientific Advisor has accused anti-GM activists of 'keeping Africa poor' [Ref: Times Online]. Other experts say GM offers no answer to the problem of global hunger and will further strengthen the hold of multinational corporations over the world's poorest farmers. Proponents of biotechnology also argue that it can deliver direct benefits to human health: for example, through the creation crops such as Golden Rice, which is modified to contain a precursor of Vitamin A and mitigate against blindness. Developments in the pipeline include GM tomatoes that contain antioxidants to improve diet [Ref: *Times* Online]; and GM soya beans containing omega-3 acids, which, it is said, could help 'prevent heart attacks' [Ref: *Times* Online].

What's the current situation in the UK?

Following the lifting of a moratorium banning GM food from countries within the European Union (EU) [Ref: BBC News] and a series of farm-scale evaluations (FSEs) [Ref: BBC News], permission to plant one variety of GM maize was granted in the UK [Ref: BBC News]. However, the maize was never planted as the company involved pulled out [Ref: BBC News], and whilst research continues, there are currently no GM crops being commercially grown [Ref: *Independent*]. Researchers argue that the delay in embracing GM has exacted heavy costs; not only has agribusiness been undermined, but

research into biotechnology has been driven out of the UK [Ref: Prospect]. But critics argue the commercial planting of GM is unnecessary and dangerous. Some suggest that a system of sustainable agriculture offers better results – higher yield and more jobs – that also protect the environment and benefit producers over corporations [Ref: Soil Association].

Is it science that's at stake, or the profits of big business?

GM supporters accuse their opponents of an anti-scientific attitude that feeds public fears and jeopardises scientific research. They emphasise the importance of the biotechnology industry in underpinning scientific progress. Environmentalists retort that all this talk about science is simply a way of distracting attention from corporations' hunger for profit.

⇨ The above information is reprinted with kind permission from the Institute of Ideas Debating Matters Competition. Visit their website at www.debatingmatters.com for more information on this and other related topics.

© Institute of Ideas Debating Matters Competition

Two-thirds want GM to be kept off their plate

Information from Friends of the Earth.

Two-thirds of people in the UK want GM crops to be kept out of the food chain, a new survey reveals today (Tuesday, 15 June 2010). Friends of the Earth and GM Freeze are urging the Government and supermarkets to listen to public opinion and take action to protect our food and farming from GM.

The GfK NOP survey for Friends of the Earth and GM Freeze also revealed that:

⇨ less than 40 per cent were aware that GM is currently creeping onto their plates via imported GM animal feed being fed to animals in British factory farms;

⇨ while there is currently no requirement for retailers to identify animal products containing GM to consumers, 89 per cent of those surveyed wanted these products to be clearly labelled;

⇨ 72 per cent would pay extra for non-GM food.

Less than 40 per cent [of survey respondents] were aware that GM is currently creeping onto their plates via imported GM animal feed being fed to animals in British factory farms

The survey comes as Friends of the Earth and GM Freeze have learnt that US-owned food retailer Asda has abandoned its commitment to GM-free eggs and poultry. The campaigning groups are calling on Asda and other supermarkets to respond to public opinion by pledging to keep GM out of the nation's meat and dairy.

Friends of the Earth's food campaigner Kirtana Chandrasekaran said:

'Despite a huge PR push by the former Government, consumers are more sceptical than ever about genetic modification, and want to be able to choose food that's guaranteed to be GM free.

'By abandoning its commitment to GM-free animal feed for chickens and sneaking GM onto its customers' plates, Asda is going against shoppers' wishes and funding animal feed plantations that are wiping out South American rainforests.

'People should tell supermarkets and their MPs to protect our food and farming from GM and support planet-friendly farming instead.'

Pete Riley of GM Freeze said:

'These results send a very clear message to Government and retailers that any weakening of policies on the import and use of GM feed will not be welcomed by the public.

'They are demanding that there should be a clear non-GM choice and are willing to pay more for it.

'Despite the rhetoric from industry and Government about the possible benefits of GM crops, the British public appears to remain very sceptical.

'Proposals from the Food Standards Agency to spend hundreds of thousands of pounds of taxpayers' money on a GM public dialogue in a crude attempt to shift public opinion on GM should now be scrapped.'

15 June 2010

⇨ The above information is reprinted with kind permission from Friends of the Earth. Visit www.foe.co.uk for more information on this and other related topics.

© Friends of the Earth

How does biotechnology address current human and environmental challenges?

Although biotechnology on its own does not have the capacity to meet the major challenges of the new millennium, it is a powerful tool for providing innovative solutions to a wide range of human and environmental issues.

Provide enough food for everyone

More than one billion people are still chronically under-nourished, and the world population is set to rise by a further 2.3 billion by mid-century. One of the Millennium Development Goals commits the 189 UN member countries to halve hunger between 1990 and 2015. To achieve this will require a substantial increase (70-100%) in global grain production. In order to increase crop yields and to expand cultivated areas as necessary, greater resistance to environmental stresses – including pathogens, drought and salinity – is essential.

In the current generation of crop biotechnology applications, certain pests can be very efficiently controlled by plants expressing Bt proteins, and more than a decade of use has shown substantial yield increases for maize and cotton. Tolerance to abiotic stress like drought or salinity is controlled by a more complex network of genes, but promising results have been achieved in model plants and are now being replicated in important food crops such as maize, wheat and rice under field conditions. In the case of drought tolerant maize, the first examples are currently being assessed by the US regulatory authorities. As well as stress tolerance, genetic modification is also proving successful in enhancing basic cellular processes to improve biomass production and plant architecture, previously considered too difficult to achieve. There is growing evidence that single gene modifications may lead to enhanced carbon fixation and partitioning into harvestable plant products.

If we are to have consistently larger harvests to feed a growing world population, plants must have both an increased yield potential and be protected from pests, diseases and environmental stresses sufficiently for increased yields to be realised in practice. Already, crop biotechnology is making a real contribution to these areas, and the potential for further improvements is significantly higher than more conventional technologies could provide.

Provide healthy food

Besides providing calories, our food must also supply essential micro-nutrients like vitamins and minerals, offer an appropriate balance between carbohydrates, proteins and fats, and ideally be free of allergens and other anti-nutritional compounds. Crop biotechnology can contribute to all areas.

A healthy diet needs to:

1 provide all essential nutrients (minerals, vitamins, essential amino acids and fatty acids, etc.) in a bio-available form;

2 be free from toxic, allergenic or anti-nutritional compounds (although in practice most food allergies are associated with staple foods such as cereals, nuts and dairy products); and

3 promote health by helping the body to defend itself against diseases and environmental stresses.

In developing countries, many millions of people have inadequate diets, often due to staple foods low in micro-nutrients (e.g. rice), or containing anti-nutritional factors (like cyanogenic cassava). In industrial countries, people look for both convenience and good nutrition in the foods they eat, although an increasing number consume too many calories, leading to obesity and further health problems. GM technology has numerous applications which can help to address these issues, a few of them being on the market but many others being at the 'proof-of-concept' stage, with encouraging results.

Examples include:

⇨ Golden rice – This technology enriches rice grains in beta-carotene, the precursor of vitamin A, the deficiency of which causes dramatic health problems in poor countries, including blindness, morbidity and child mortality.

⇨ Bio-fortification – This addresses malnutrition by increasing the concentrations of essential minerals, especially iron and zinc, in the edible portions of crops. GM can also be used to eliminate anti-nutrients, like phytic acid, which sequesters minerals and makes them unavailable for digestion.

⇨ Heart-healthy oils – Soybean has been genetically modified to produce an oil with an increased ratio of monounsaturated/polyunsaturated fatty acids. This avoids the need for chemical hydrogenation of the oil before using it in processed food and overcomes the associated drawbacks regarding human health (increase in blood cholesterol). Other varieties have

EUROPABIO

been modified to express high levels of omega-3 fatty acids, normally only available in significant quantities from oily fish or food supplements.

⇨ Increasing the content of essential amino acids – Maize grains are naturally deficient in lysine, an essential amino acid for animal diets, and genetic modification has been used to correct this. This innovation is dedicated to livestock feed but is a 'proof-of-concept' that re-balancing foodstuffs in essential amino acids is feasible via biotechnology.

Preserve water resources

Agriculture consumes 70% of total freshwater reserves, a renewable but finite resource. Once, water shortages were rarely associated with northern European climates. Today, however, DG Agriculture's report entitled *Adaption to Climate Change: the Challenge for European Agriculture and Rural Areas* clearly outlines concerns for the future. Published in April 2009, the document outlines that high water-stress areas are expected to increase from 19% today to 35% by 2070, implying 'significant changes in the quality and availability of water resources'. http://europa.eu/rapid/pressReleasesAction.do?reference=MEMO/09/145&format=HTML&aged=0&language=EN&guiLanguage=en. This is contextualised by the information that more than 80% of EU farmland is currently rain-fed.

Among the challenging objectives of sustainable development, bigger harvests need to be produced while less water is consumed. This is what scientists call increasing 'water use efficiency' (WUE) and intensive research is dedicated to identification of the genes controlling the trait in model and crop species and manipulation to reduce water needs. There has already been some success, via both conventional or molecular marker-assisted breeding, and r-DNA technology. Here are some examples of GM applications currently in development:

Using water efficiency

⇨ Plants control both water transpiration to the atmosphere and carbon dioxide uptake from the atmosphere via the same openings in the leaves, called stomata. The control of stomata density and opening is critical to WUE and some of the key genes involved have been isolated and manipulated to increase the ratio of biomass produced to the amount of water transpired.

Controlling carbon dioxide

⇨ Carbon dioxide fixation by photosynthesis follows different pathways, with different water use efficiencies. The conversion of less efficient (C3) crops to more efficient (C4) ones by shifting their photosynthetic type was once considered impossible, but is now being actively pursued by a rice research

consortium under the umbrella of the International Rice Research Institute (IRRI) in the Philippines. C4 crops have the added advantage of having higher yield potential.

Protecting soil water

⇨ Water released from fields to the atmosphere is the sum of the water transpired by the plants and of the water directly evaporated by the soil. It is important to maximise the first portion and to minimise the second, and this ratio depends on the way plants colonise the soil with their roots and cover the soil with their leaves. Genes controlling root and leaf growth and architecture are being isolated and functionally tested in model and crop plants, providing increased yields with limited water loss from the soil. The current use of herbicide-tolerant crops as an essential component of no-till farming also helps to reduce water loss from the soil.

Reduce soil erosion

Weed control is essential for crop productivity. Mechanical cultivation, or tillage, aims to kill weeds by disturbing their roots and burying them before sowing, but ploughing has disadvantages. It makes the soil susceptible to erosion and increases carbon loss to the atmosphere, depleting the organic matter which is important for protecting and maintaining the fertility of soil. Reduced tillage is only feasible when efficient alternative weed control strategies are available. GM herbicide-tolerance is an ideal trait to encourage reduced tillage, as a cost-effective, labour-saving and environmentally friendly strategy. The technology has been adopted by farmers with an unprecedented rapidity since the mid-1990s. For soybean, the no-till area has nearly doubled in the US and a five-fold increase was recorded in Argentina, with Roundup Ready® varieties estimated to account for 95% of the no-till soybean area. Besides soil preservation, no-tillage agriculture reduces use of fossil fuels, saving the farmer money and reducing the environmental impact of intensive farming.

Protect biodiversity

Biodiversity is a term covering the variety and extent of all forms of life, including microbes, plants and animals, and varies from area to area. The mix of species is different on farmland than in the wild, and specific crops and the way they are managed can have a big influence on this. The use of GM crops is just another variable among many, and there is no simple general relationship between GMOs and farmland biodiversity.

In an attempt to study the impact of herbicide-tolerant crops on biodiversity in a controlled way, a team of scientists conducted on-farm studies in the UK, monitoring biodiversity within GM and non-GM fields

of maize, sugar beet and oilseed rape, including field margins, over several years. The main conclusion was that each combination of GM crop with its environment is a special case that behaves in its own way and that GMOs can not be viewed globally as either decreasing or increasing biodiversity in the agricultural systems studied. The different crops (i.e. the difference between a crop – whether GM or otherwise – of oilseed rape and a maize or sugar beet crop) themselves had the biggest influence on biodiversity.

However, plant biotechnology provides opportunities to conserve biodiversity:

⇨ Some GM crops resist insect attack by producing a natural insecticide, the so-called Bt protein (derived from a soil bacterium itself used as a pesticide in organic farming). The advantage over conventional spraying of insecticides is that the Bt toxin only kills those pests that feed on the plant, and has no impact on the non-target insects in the field. In contrast, the spraying of insecticides may be harmful to some non-target organisms.

⇨ By increasing crop productivity on existing farmland, GM technology reduces the need to encroach on wilderness or marginal land, so preserving natural habitats.

⇨ By sustaining crop productivity and combating the natural enemies of crop plants, GM technology may also help to preserve endangered crop species. This was exemplified in Hawaii by papaya cultivation, which was in danger of being wiped out by a virus.

Produce biomaterials

Plants can make a broad range of renewable materials starting with the basic photosynthetic process of forming sugars from atmospheric carbon dioxide using the energy of sunlight. Since they are alternatives to raw materials derived from fossil fuels, this makes them especially valuable in the context of sustainable development and of the new 'bioeconomy', in which chemical processes will increasingly be replaced by biological ones.

For example, plants have been genetically modified to produce plastics such as polyhydroxybutyrate, a biodegradable polyester which can be a substitute for polypropylene. Although this was a technical success in both model and crop plants (including mustard, cotton and maize), the economic feasibility of the approach has still to be worked out. Another approach for the production of biomaterials from renewable plant resources is to use plant carbohydrates as starting material for fermentation.

The industrial uses of starch potatoes have long been exploited. Examples where the potato has been genetically modified to produce more of the right materials are now close to the market.

Biodegradable polylactic acid is a useful polymer and fibre already produced cost-effectively on a commercial scale for a number of years. Starting with a fermentable carbon source, an enormous range of useful materials can be produced, and it is here that we see the synergy between green (plant) and white (industrial) biotechnology.

Plant biotechnology can also be used to tailor the structure of plant carbohydrates to modify their physicochemical properties and facilitate industrial processing. High-amylopectin potatoes have been developed, for example, producing starch ideally suited to industrial processing. Cellulose is the most abundant plant polymer, with large quantities being used to make paper. Genetic modification of poplar trees is being used to make wood pulp extraction less polluting, by reducing the level of lignin, a phenolic polymer which is tightly bound to cellulose and needs to be removed by aggressive chemical processing.

Production of pharmaceuticals and vaccines

Plants have been used as sources of pharmaceuticals across the millennia, but modern biotechnology has opened a new era in the exploitation of plants for preventing and curing diseases. In particular, there are two main advantages to the production of therapeutic proteins and vaccines in plants:

⇨ the efficiency of plants as protein factories, compared to microbial or animal cell culture, although the overall cost-effectiveness of the process has to be evaluated on a case-by-case basis;

⇨ product safety, as plant-derived pharmaceuticals do not contain the infectious agents that may contaminate drugs extracted from human or animal cell culture.

EUROPABIO

There are currently three types of application:

⇨ therapeutic proteins including haemoglobins, anticoagulants, enzymes (e.g. lipases or b-gluco-cerebrosidases), peptide hormones (e.g. insulin or somatropin), antiviral or antibacterial peptides (e.g. interferons and lactoferrin);

⇨ antibodies (e.g. against a bacterial agent of tooth decay, *Streptococcus mutans*);

⇨ vaccines (e.g. against Hepatitis B or intestinal bacteria causing infantile diarrhoea, a common cause of child death in developing countries).

A particularly challenging project aims to fight diseases widespread in the tropics, like Hepatitis B, by developing edible vaccines, which do not require cold storage. Banana is one of the major food crops which are envisaged as vehicles for this novel oral vaccination strategy. The efficacy of edible vaccines in banana or potato has now been demonstrated and the next challenge is to take these novel products to market. Practical issues to be addressed include efficient segregation from their traditional food counterparts, clear traceability rules and appropriate patient information.

Produce biofuels

Biofuels are plant-derived alternatives to fossil fuels, currently mainly bioethanol and biodiesel. Bioethanol, today used in blends with petrol, is made by the fermentation of plant sugars (often starting from starch) while biodiesel is produced by esterification of oil from crops such as rapeseed, palm or soybean. Worldwide energy consumption is expected to grow by 50% by 2025, much of this mushrooming demand being driven by developing countries. The European Union has a target of having 6% of biomass-derived fuels in its total fuel consumption by 2010. This target needs strong political commitments and economic incentives, as well as multi-disciplinary efforts to make such a scenario technically feasible. However, concerns about the sustainability of some of the current sources of biofuels are holding back progress.

Plant biotechnology will be an important tool for developing high-yielding energy crops, allowing the cost-efficient transformation of their biomass into biofuels. The current generation of biofuels competes with food production, but the future use of biomass and dedicated energy crops will provide a more sustainable supply. High crop yields can be obtained by optimising plant architecture (optimal light capture), by extending the lifespan of the light-capturing leaves, by controlling development (delayed or suppressed flowering, which is a highly energy-consuming process), and by avoiding biomass losses due to pathogen attacks and post-harvest diseases. Energy crops should also have suitable compositional properties (sugar and oil contents)

and the raw materials they provide should be readily accessible for industrial processing (easy fractionation of lignin and cellulose, for instance). At each of these levels, gene transfer technologies (combined with other breeding techniques) may prove very powerful. The selection of novel, annual or perennial crops specially dedicated to the supply of renewable energy will need rapid gene identification and recombination strategies using biotechnology.

Mitigate the rise of atmospheric CO_2 and global warming

Agriculture is a significant contributor to the emission of greenhouse gases, including carbon dioxide, methane and nitrous oxide. At the same time, carbon dioxide is sequestered in plant biomass, and the lifetime and the decomposition rate of organic matter will influence the carbon balance between the terrestrial ecosystems and the atmosphere. Because of the pressing need to reduce emissions of greenhouse gases to mitigate global warming, changes in agricultural practices may be needed. After more than a decade of GM crop cultivation, it is possible to draw conclusions about its effects on greenhouse gas emission and CO_2 sequestration:

⇨ By facilitating no-till and conservation tillage systems, GM technology reduces tractor use and fuel consumption. Due to the efficacy of post-emergence weed control permitted by herbicide-tolerance technology, a significant number of farmers have moved to such management systems.

⇨ GM technology contributes to a higher level of carbon sequestration in biomass, as conservation tillage results in increased soil organic matter. This cropping system also reduces the emission of other greenhouse gases, like nitrous oxide, released in the atmosphere as a side effect of nitrogen fertilisation, as conservation tillage systems allow lower levels of fertiliser use.

⇨ In 2007, the permanent carbon dioxide savings from reduced fuel use was the equivalent of removing nearly 0.5 million cars from the road for a year and the additional soil carbon sequestration gains were equivalent to removing nearly 5.8 million cars from the roads. In total, this was equal to about 17% of all registered cars in the UK. As use of GM crops continues to increase, so will reductions in greenhouse gas emissions.

⇨ The above information is reprinted with kind permission from EuropaBio. Visit www.europabio.org for more information.

© *EuropaBio*

Ten reasons why we don't need GM foods

With the cost of food recently skyrocketing – hitting not just shoppers but the poor and hungry in the developing world – genetically modified (GM) foods are once again being promoted as the way to feed the world. But this is little short of a confidence trick. Far from needing more GM foods, there are urgent reasons why we need to ban them altogether.

1. GM foods won't solve the food crisis

A 2008 World Bank report concluded that increased biofuel production is the major cause of the increase in food prices. GM giant Monsanto has been at the heart of the lobbying for biofuels (crops grown for fuel rather than food) – while profiting enormously from the resulting food crisis and using it as a PR opportunity to promote GM foods!

'The climate crisis was used to boost biofuels, helping to create the food crisis; and now the food crisis is being used to revive the fortunes of the GM industry' – Daniel Howden, Africa correspondent of *The Independent*

'The cynic in me thinks that they're just using the current food crisis and the fuel crisis as a springboard to push GM crops back on to the public agenda. I understand why they're doing it, but the danger is that if they're making

So full of promise, ...or promises!

these claims about GM crops solving the problem of drought or feeding the world, that's bulls**t' – Professor Denis Murphy, Head of Biotechnology at the University of Glamorgan in Wales

2. GM crops do not increase yield potential

Despite the promises, GM has not increased the yield potential of any commercialised crops. In fact, studies show that the most widely-grown GM crop, GM soya, has suffered reduced yields.

A report that analysed nearly two decades worth of peer-reviewed research on the yield of the primary GM food/feed crops, soybeans and corn (maize), reveals that despite 20 years of research and 13 years of commercialisation, genetic engineering has failed to significantly increase US crop yields. The author, former US EPA and US FDA biotech specialist Dr Gurian-Sherman, concludes that when it comes to yield, 'Traditional breeding outperforms genetic engineering hands down. Let's be clear. As of this year [2008], there are no commercialised GM crops that inherently increase yield. Similarly, there are no GM crops on the market that were engineered to resist drought, reduce fertiliser pollution or save soil. Not one.'

3. GM crops increase pesticide use

US Government data shows that in the US, GM crops have produced an overall increase, not decrease, in pesticide use compared to conventional crops.

'The promise was that you could use less chemicals and produce a greater yield. But let me tell you none of this is true' – Bill Christison, President of the US National Family Farm Coalition

4. There are better ways to feed the world

A major UN/World Bank-sponsored report compiled by 400 scientists and endorsed by 58 countries concluded that GM crops have little to offer global agriculture and the challenges of poverty, hunger and climate change, because better alternatives are available. In particular, the report championed 'agroecological' farming as the sustainable way forward for developing countries.

5. Other farm technologies are more successful

Integrated Pest Management and other innovative low-input or organic methods of controlling pests and boosting yields have proven highly effective, particularly in the developing world. Other plant breeding technologies, such as Marker Assisted Selection (non-GM genetic mapping), are widely expected to boost global agricultural productivity more effectively and safely than GM.

'The quiet revolution is happening in gene mapping, helping us understand crops better. That is up and running and could have a far greater impact on agriculture [than GM]' – Professor John Snape, head of the Department of Crop Genetics, John Innes Centre

6. GM foods have not been shown to be safe to eat

Genetic modification is a crude and imprecise way of incorporating foreign genetic material (e.g. from viruses, bacteria) into crops, with unpredictable consequences. The resulting GM foods have undergone little rigorous and no long-term safety testing, but animal feeding tests have shown worrying health effects. Only one study has been published on the direct effects on humans of eating a GM food. It found unexpected effects on gut bacteria, but was never followed up.

It is claimed that Americans have eaten GM foods for years with no ill effects. But these foods are unlabelled in the US and no one has monitored the consequences. With other novel foods like trans fats, it has taken decades to realise that they have caused millions of premature deaths.

'We are confronted with the most powerful technology the world has ever known, and it is being rapidly deployed with almost no thought whatsoever to its consequences' – Dr Suzanne Wuerthele, US Environmental Protection Agency (EPA) toxicologist

7. Stealth GMOs in animal feed – without consumers' consent

Meat, eggs and dairy products from animals raised on the millions of tons of GM feed imported into Europe do not have to be labelled. Some studies have shown that contrary to GM and food industry claims, animals raised on GM feed ARE different from those raised on non-GM feed. Other studies show that if GM crops are fed to animals, GM material can appear in the resulting products and that the animals' health can be affected. So eating 'stealth GMOs' may affect the health of consumers.

8. GM crops are a long-term economic disaster for farmers

A 2009 report showed that GM seed prices in America have increased dramatically, compared to non-GM and organic seeds, cutting average farm incomes for US farmers growing GM crops. The report concluded, 'At the present time there is a massive disconnect between the sometimes lofty rhetoric from those championing biotechnology as the proven path toward global food security and what is actually happening on farms in the US that have grown dependent on GM seeds and are now dealing with the consequences.'

9. GM and non-GM cannot co-exist

GM contamination of conventional and organic food is increasing. An unapproved GM rice that was grown for only one year in field trials was found to have extensively contaminated the US rice supply and seed stocks. In Canada, the organic oilseed rape industry has been destroyed by contamination from GM rape. In Spain, a study found that GM maize 'has caused a drastic reduction in organic cultivations of this grain and is making their coexistence practically impossible'.

> *Genetic modification is a crude and imprecise way of incorporating foreign genetic material into crops, with unpredictable consequences*

The time has come to choose between a GM-based, or a non-GM-based, world food supply.

'If some people are allowed to choose to grow, sell and consume GM foods, soon nobody will be able to choose food, or a biosphere, free of GM. It's a one-way choice, like the introduction of rabbits or cane toads to Australia; once it's made, it can't be reversed' – Roger Levett, specialist in sustainable development

10. We can't trust GM companies

The big biotech firms pushing their GM foods have a terrible history of toxic contamination and public deception. GM is attractive to them because it gives them patents that allow monopoly control over the world's food supply. They have taken to harassing and intimidating farmers for the 'crime' of saving patented seed or 'stealing' patented genes – even if those genes got into the farmer's fields through accidental contamination by wind or insects.

'Farmers are being sued for having GMOs on their property that they did not buy, do not want, will not use and cannot sell' – Tom Wiley, North Dakota farmer

⇨ Information from bangmfood.org. Visit their website at www.bangmfood.org for more information on this and other related topics, or to view references for this article.

© *bangmfood.org*

Why can't we make a decision about the genetic modification of foods and crops?

Derek Burke diagnoses the problem and suggests a solution.

David Willetts, Minister for Universities and Science, said at the British Science Festival on 14 September: 'I'm announcing today that the GM dialogue project will not continue in its current format. However, it's vital to engage people of all ages on scientific issues, so that they have a real say about developments which can affect all of us.'

This is the second public dialogue process on genetically modified food and crops to fail to produce an agreed outcome. The first – the GMNation? Debate – was abandoned because of a lack of consensus, and the second seems to have run into a similar problem. In both cases, people with very different views about genetically modified foods and crops have been unable to agree. Why is this?

Safe but not on sale

It's now 16 years since the first two foods derived from genetically modified plants were approved as safe to eat. The first was a puree from genetically modified tomatoes, which went on sale in the UK, labelled and allowing for consumer choice. The second was the meal from genetically modified soya beans. Both were recommended for approval in 1994, and the Minister agreed to both.

The Zeneca tomato puree outsold the existing product, but was removed from sale, not for safety reasons, but because of activist and political pressure on the supermarkets. The GM soya never reached the shelves. A great deal of UK research and development on GM crops went to the US, and no product labelled GM is on sale in the UK today.

However, meat from cattle fed genetically modified soya is widely sold, chickens are likely to follow suit, and we are told that it is impossible to exclude genetically modified soya and corn from all other processed food products on sale because of its ubiquity. So it's safe but not on sale, and it looks as if without a steer from government, retailers will never move.

So why was the launch of GM products such a fiasco?

Anti campaign

Looking back, it seems pretty clear it was because of a campaign run by several non-governmental organisations and some newspapers. The first major public event, a television broadcast on 11 August 1998, and then a press conference held in the House of Commons on 12 February 1999, was the claim made by Arpad Pusztai and collaborators that transgenic potatoes had stunted growth and suppressed immunity in rats that had eaten transgenic potatoes for 110 days.

His statements were generalised by the press, their writers asserting that all GM foods could be unsafe. Despite the fact that there was no published data to support the claim, and despite an independent review which cleared the product (October 1998), and a robust response from the Prime Minister (20 February 1999), we scientists were left challenging these claims in the media as best we could – the Science Media Centre was yet unborn. We faced a professional public relations campaign with a new headline every two or three days; and we were soon on the defensive. 'So, Professor Burke, you can't prove that GM soya is absolutely safe?' I was asked live on TV. 'Well, no,' was my slightly naive response. 'So the British public is being subjected to an untested new product made by genetic modification which is claimed to cause cancer?' End of interview.

Our mistake was not lack of effort but, rather coming fresh out of our laboratories, most of us were not sufficiently skilled and experienced to counter the onslaught mounted

by the pressure groups and fanned by the media. The genie could not be put back into the bottle.

So what are the possibilities?

Do nothing

'Minister,' I can hear a senior civil servant saying, 'the UK faces a very difficult financial future and we have to make many difficult decisions. Why bother ourselves with an issue like this which is not of primary importance?'

Surely that is a policy of despair, not worthy of an administration which is determined to lead Britain in a new direction. We used to think that we might be able to earn our living by what came out of the City, but no longer, and as a small island trading nation on the edge of a large land mass, we need to exploit and invest in our excellent science and technology if we are to continue to earn our living.

Try again

'After all,' Ministers must say to themselves, 'surely if we get fifteen sensible people in a room, talking to each other for long enough, a consensus will emerge.'

That was not true of the GMNation? Debate, in which I was peripherally involved. It wasn't true of the EU:US Biotechnology Consultative Forum in 2000, of which I was a member, and I understand it's the problem with the current process which has just been terminated. The problem is that there are members of these committees with non-negotiable positions, and since a consensus is required, deadlock is inevitable.

Mark Henderson, the science editor for *The Times*, put it well recently thus: 'When I took part in an online debate about GM food with Emma Hockridge of the Soil Association, I thought I'd explore a little farther. What evidence, I asked, would be sufficient to convince this organic lobby group to accept that genetic engineering was neither unsafe nor environmentally damaging? I asked again. And again. I never got an answer.'[1]

The EU option

Recently, Commissioner Dalli has proposed to delegate decisions over GM down to individual countries – subsidiarity in practice. However, this raises wide issues of principle in Brussels, and I think is unlikely to be adopted in the near term.

A way forward

So what's left? The problem is not lack of evidence, or lack of informed reports; for example from the Nuffield Council on Bioethics,[2,3] from the Royal Society,[4] from the UK Government GM Science Review or from proponents of both the pro- and the anti-position. The problem is that they cannot agree, because at least some of them have non-negotiable positions.

I suggest we need an independent process which sifts the scientific evidence and makes a recommendation to the Minister. This procedure has been used in the past to resolve similar apparently intractable problems such as the siting of a nuclear power station, the building of an airport runway or a new wind farm, but in this case it should be given a deadline. We have already spent enough time on this problem.

So I propose a type of judicial inquiry in which the evidence is reviewed, in public, with evidence in person or in writing, from proponents of the different positions. The evidence should be weighed by people drawn from those professions trained to weigh evidence and I suggest a panel of assessors chaired by a judge.

But the difficulty, too complex to be resolved in this short article, is how wide ranging to make the review. Is it a debate only about issues of relevance to UK agriculture, a review of the scientific evidence in relation to human health and environmental issues, or a wider discussion about the whole agricultural enterprise? I favour the first. Recommendations should be made in public, and the Minister should respond in public. Thus the Minister makes the decision on the basis of evidence sifted and weighed by a panel of relevant expert assessors, but who, crucially, do not have a position themselves. The responsibility for the final decision must lie with the Minister.

References

1   Ideas not just for dummies. *Eureka, The Times*, September 2010, p9.

2   Genetically modified crops: the ethical and social issues. Nuffield Council on Bioethics, 1999.

3   The use of genetically modified crops in developing countries. Nuffield Council on Bioethics, 2004.

4   Reaping the benefits: Science and the sustainable intensification of global agriculture. The Royal Society, October 2009. www.gmsciencedebate.org.uk/report/ default.htm#second

Professor Derek Burke is a former chair of the Advisory Committee on Novel Foods and Processes (1989-97), a former Vice-Chancellor of the University of East Anglia (1987-95), and a former member of BBSRC's Bioscience for Society Panel (2007-10).

December 2010

⇨ The above information is an extract from the December 2010 issue of the British Science Association's *People & Science* newsletter, and is reprinted with permission. Visit www.britishscienceassociation.org for more information on this and other topics.

© British Science Association

BRITISH SCIENCE ASSOCIATION

GM crops – the risks explained

There has been much debate over the adoption of genetically modified crops in the UK. In this article we address some of the commonly identified issues and offer our own 'smiley based' risk assessment.

Our smiley guide to risk

Negligible risk   Low risk   Some risk   High risk

GM foods may be poisonous to animals and humans

Before a GM food can reach the shops it will have been subject to extensive regulation and analysis, way beyond anything that our non-GM diet has ever been subjected to. But even if that is not enough, our everyday diet consists of around 6,000 different chemicals which we are perfectly able to deal with through digestion. Most of these chemicals have been created naturally in the biochemical pathways of living organisms and it is very unlikely that GM crops are going to alter the fundamentals of nature and expose us to anything new. Millions of Americans have been eating GM crops for some years without ill effect, which seems to prove the point.

GM crops may be harmful to beneficial insects

In practice, GM crops will only include genes that produce an insecticide where a significant pest problem exists already. In such cases the GM crop is likely to be less harmful to beneficial insects because less manufactured insecticide will need to be applied.

In laboratory experiments in the US it has been shown that the pollen from maize plants that were bred to contain an insecticide, BT toxin,* was able to kill the caterpillar of the Monarch butterfly. While this was indicative of laboratory risk, in the real world the risks are much lower as the Monarch caterpillars rarely eat maize pollen.

*BT toxin is a natural insecticide and the gene comes from a soil bacterium. The toxin is widely used by organic farmers and is poisonous to caterpillars but affects few other insects and is harmless to fish and mammals.

GM crops may contaminate other nearby crops

There is certainly a risk that this can happen and producers growing a traditional crop variety under an organic system might find their production system compromised by a GM crop nearby. We believe that Defra should keep a watching brief on this but we do not consider it a major risk when one considers the amount of admix (non-crop material) that is harvested with a crop (especially an organic one).

GM crops may encourage resistant weeds and pests

Yes, but resistant weeds and pests have been the story of agriculture for the last 10,000 years. GM technology is another development that farmers might adopt and if this leads to resistance, farmers will have to revert to their more traditional methods of control.

UK AGRICULTURE

An artificial gene may leak out into wild plants

Yes, but there is nothing to say that this won't happen with non-GM crops anyway. All crops are selectively bred for improved characteristics and these could just as easily escape. Don't forget too that the artificial gene in the crop is already 'out there'.

GM crops may lead to a reduction in biodiversity

This argument is usually advanced on the grounds that herbicide-resistant crops can be sprayed with a herbicide like glyphosate, which will result in the complete kill of weeds. Of course, in practice farmers never seek a complete kill of weeds because that requires too much expensive herbicide. It is much more likely that farmers will try to use as little herbicide as possible and this may lead to generally weedier and more biodiverse conditions. If the weed burden does become excessive, farmers will know that they can still deal with the problem without killing the crop – a situation that does not exist in conventional systems.

Too much of a GM crop may be a bad thing

Yes, it would be foolish to plant a single variety of a GM crop too widely only to find that it was particularly exposed to adverse circumstances that arose. Diversification is the key to minimising risk and in agriculture that means using differing varieties within rotations. This applies to GM crops just as it does to conventional farming systems.

GM crops may lead to greater farmer dependency upon agribusiness

Farmers will choose the farming system that most easily helps them to make a profit and meet the demands of their customers. If this does result in a greater dependency on agribusiness, does this matter?

GM crops may offer no advantage over other farming systems

Then farmers won't use them.

GM technology is producer-driven rather than consumer-sought

If GM technology produces solutions for our needs then the technology will be adopted. It doesn't really matter much whether this was producer driven or consumer sought – the marketplace will decide whether it succeeds.

Something unexpected may catch us out

Absolutely, and in our view almost everyone has missed the point about the risk. The real risk of GM crops comes not within the food and farming environment which is entirely artificial, but from taking a beneficial biochemical pathway from an organism in the wild and then exposing it to the competitive pressure inherent within agricultural systems. If the pathway which has served the wild organism breaks down in the agricultural environment, the same may happen in the wild with obviously serious effects.

⇨ The above information is reprinted with kind permission from UK Agriculture. Visit www.ukagriculture. com for more information.

© UK Agriculture

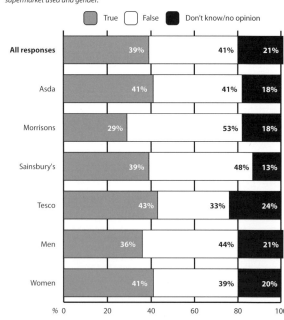

GM-fed products
Respondents were told: 'I am now going to read out a statement, and I would like you to tell me whether you think this is true, or not. "Most of the animal products, such as milk, dairy, eggs, meat or fish products, that are sold in Britain come from animals that have been fed on a diet containing GM (genetically modified) ingredients." Do you think this is true or false?' By supermarket used and gender.

Legend: True | False | Don't know/no opinion

	True	False	Don't know/no opinion
All responses	39%	41%	21%
Asda	41%	41%	18%
Morrisons	29%	53%	18%
Sainsbury's	39%	48%	13%
Tesco	43%	33%	24%
Men	36%	44%	21%
Women	41%	39%	20%

Fieldwork: 4-6 June 2010. Base: 1000. Source: GfK/NOP opinion survey on GM-fed labels. Carried out for Friends of the Earth England, Wales and Northern Ireland. Data taken from the GM Freeze website: www.gmfreeze.org

UK AGRICULTURE

Consumer benefits of GM crops

GM crops have been grown extensively around the world for the last 13 years, and two trillion meals with GM ingredients have been eaten with no substantiated evidence of harm to health. Last year, over 13 million farmers in 25 different countries planted over 125 million hectares of GM crops, including maize, soybeans, oilseed rape and even papayas; that is more than four times the land area of the British Isles. The question for people in the UK is: how does this help me?

To date, most GM crop production has addressed the productivity, availability and cost of food supplies, and hence has no clearly visible or easily identifiable consumer benefit. This is now changing, with specific consumer benefits close to market.

Healthier oils and foods

⇨ Omega-3 fatty acids, commonly found in oily fish and widely known for their health benefits in helping to fight cardiovascular disease, are now contained within GM soybeans currently under development. These soybeans will be processed into soya oil (often sold as 'vegetable oil') and used to provide a range of foods with significant health benefits.[1]

⇨ A GM tomato supplemented with genes from snapdragon flowers (rich in an antioxidant called anthocyanin), developed by the John Innes Centre, could have cancer-fighting properties.

⇨ Golden Rice, fortified with increased levels of pro-vitamin A, is now at the advanced field trial stage of development in the Philippines, and is now supported by the Gates Foundation.

⇨ Researchers in Cambridge have produced a type of GM wheat that releases fewer calories into the body compared to other varieties currently available.[2]

The potential for allergy-free foods

⇨ Scientists have identified a new gene in peanuts that codes for a protein with no apparent allergic effects, research that opens up the possibility of allergen-free GM nuts.[3]

Food with a lower carbon footprint

⇨ In the UK, agriculture accounts for 7% of all carbon emissions; the use of GM technology can help in reducing the carbon footprint and environmental impact of farming in a number of ways.

⇨ GM crops can help decrease the need for ploughing, helping farmers adopt less-intensive agricultural methods and so further reducing the carbon footprint of the food chain.

⇨ GM crops are being developed that require 50% less fertiliser, a major part of the carbon footprint of a crop.

Protecting fruits and vegetables from disease

⇨ In the UK, recent trials have been successfully undertaken of GM potatoes with intrinsic resistance to devastating diseases such as blight.

⇨ Papayas genetically modified to resist Ringspot-Virus (a disease that can sharply lower yields) are being grown in the US and Canada, greatly increasing the quantity of papayas available for consumption and exported abroad, and saving one of Hawaii's major industries.

In the UK, recent trials have been successfully undertaken of GM potatoes with intrinsic resistance to devastating diseases such as blight

⇨ Several international institutes are developing apples with resistance to dozens of different diseases including fire blight, apple scab and powdery mildew. With conventional breeding the production of scab-resistant varieties of good eating quality and suitability for commercial production can take as long as 50 years.[4]

Consumer attitudes to GM foods

Consumer choice is about ensuring that people have the opportunity to buy the widest possible range of products according to their own tastes and requirements. That right to choose should include GM foods. Likewise, farmers should have the opportunity to grow GM crops along with organic and non-GM, so providing consumers with genuine choice and an ability to benefit from them if they so choose.

Much consumer attitude research fails to qualify a simple yes/no response by a level of relative importance. In

AGRICULTURAL BIOTECHNOLOGY COUNCIL

contrast to many claims, the majority of consumers do not regard GM as a major concern despite attempts from those opposed to the technology to make it a polarised debate. This is highlighted by an EU report published last year, which showed that where GM is on the shelf, it sells;[6] nevertheless, there remains a significant gap in consumer knowledge about how the technology works.

Consumers are starting to recognise the benefits

⇨ An IGD report (2008) suggests that a majority of consumers do recognise that there are important potential benefits of GM crops.[7]

⇨ 52% of those polled believed that GM can be used to increase productivity and feed a growing world population, while only 13% disagreed.

⇨ Additionally, 47% of consumers thought that GM can help to protect crops against disease and extreme weather.

The majority of consumers remain undecided, but most are unconcerned

⇨ Research by the Food Standards Agency in 2009 suggests that UK consumers do not have a strong interest in GM: only 6% of those surveyed expressed unprompted concern about GM food.[8]

⇨ In summer 2008, after a high level of media coverage of the GM debate, IGD tested the level of support and opposition towards GM foods in the UK. The largest proportion of respondents (54%) neither supported nor opposed GM. A further 29% expressed a mild opinion and only 14% were strongly opposed to GM.[9]

However, there is still a lack of understanding about how the technology works

⇨ IGD[10] tested the level of perceived knowledge of GM foods amongst consumers. Just under half (48%) believed that their knowledge was 'poor' or 'very poor'. Just 7% were able to give an accurate definition of GM.

Public discussion of GM is based on a low understanding of what it is, and deliberate attempts to cause confusion, which is restricting progress in understanding and opinion, and a failure to engage the public in a meaningful debate.

abc wishes to work in partnership to ensure this knowledge gap is filled, such that consumers can take knowledge-based decisions on the food that they choose to buy and eat.

References

1 http://www.timesonline.co.uk/tol/news/uk/science/article5068437.ece

2 http://www.independent.co.uk/news/science/why-monsanto-thinks-its-gm-wheat-isthe-next-best-thing-for-sliced-bread-702164.html

3 http://www.foodnavigator-usa.com/Science-Nutrition/Peanut-gene-breakthroughmay-lead-to-allergen-free-nuts

4 http://greenbio.checkbiotech.org/news/gm_work_boosts_apple_disease_resistance

5 GM crops: the first ten years – Global socio-economic and environmental impacts, Barfoot, P. and Brookes, G. (2006)

6 http://www.kcl.ac.uk/consumerchoice

7 Genetically Modified Foods – Consumer Research, IGD, October 2008

8 FSA tracker survey, May 2009

9 Genetically Modified Foods – Consumer Research, IGD, October 2008

10 Genetically Modified Foods – Consumer Research, IGD, October 2008

⇨ The above information is reprinted with kind permission from the Agricultural Biotechnology Council. Visit www.abcinformation.org for more information on this and other related topics.

AGRICULTURAL BIOTECHNOLOGY COUNCIL

Just because GM is gaining popularity doesn't make it right

The Government has warmed to the idea of genetically modified food but sceptics are right to raise concerns.

By Lucy Siegle

To approve or not to approve? The transgenic question is back in the form of the super salmon or the Frankenfish (which sobriquet you pick depends on how GM-tolerant you are). Take a growth gene from another type of salmon, mix with a bit of DNA from the eel-like ocean pout, as US biotech firm, AquaBounty has done, and you get a creature with all the appearance of an Atlantic salmon that is actually produced in a giant, inland tank. AquaBounty has spent 15 years trying to get US regulators to approve the advanced hybrid fish for supermarket shelves and now appears to be very close.

The engineered salmon represents a watershed moment for GM foods as a whole. For one thing, it is the first animal to get this far. If and when it's approved, it will join the 180-plus transgenic crop 'events', involving 15 traits that have been deregulated or approved in one of 27 countries. Earlier this year, a 12-year European stalemate on approving GM crops (politely called a moratorium) came to an end when power to approve was devolved to individual nations. GM's fortunes are looking up.

Acceptance of GM varies from country to country. In Europe, Sweden and the Netherlands are considered pro GM and Germany and Austria are considered staunchly against. On the surface, the UK has appeared hostile. The Flavr Savr tomato (the rotting gene was removed) was approved for sale in the UK, but its arrival was pre-empted by hysterical protest about GM ingredients and it never made it to the shops. And all the 54 GM crop trials attempted since 2000 have been torn up by protesters and no GM crops are grown commercially.

However, behind the scenes there's some serious *rapprochement* going on.

Peter Melchett, policy director of the Soil Association and Britain's most famous crop trasher, who famously pulled up six-and-a-half acres of GM maize in 1999, says that £20 million of taxpayers' money has gone into GM crop research since 1997, despite the fact that not a single crop is grown in the UK.

If New Labour noticeably warmed to the idea of GM, the new Government is showing even more love. One of the first acts by the Coalition (anti-GM wags point out that this is in itself an unnatural hybrid) was to approve a Leeds University crop trial of GM potatoes. Meanwhile, Environment Minister Caroline Spelman is the former director of a biotechnology lobbying group.

We are still far from wholesale consumer acceptance of GM, but listen and you'll hear people beginning to shift their position. GM is gaining currency as a pragmatic solution to food security and even an environmentally responsible way of providing food and fuel. It's reminiscent of the extraordinary volte-face about nuclear energy, from classic eco-campaigning territory to a climate change-adaptation technique. We haven't yet heard from the big-name environmental recanters as we did with nuclear but the signs of change are there. The award-winning environmental writer Richard Girling has argued 'that GM crops are good for people and good for the planet'.

But we should be careful not to throw caution or transgenic materials to the wind. While Frankenfood arguments overplay risks to human health, many GM concerns are important. The worst-case scenario would be that we feel under pressure to acquiesce.

There is a tendency to depict anyone with reservations about GM as a Gaia-fearing lunatic. 'The pro-GM lobby

has done a fantastic job in persuading the media and politicians that even the most modest GM-scepticism is tantamount to extreme science-hating emotionalism,' Jonathon Porritt has written. 'To express any reservations about the notional sustainability benefits of current GM crops, let alone about the massively hyped potential benefits of future GM products, is to open oneself up to the charge of debilitating technophobia.'

At the risk of inviting such charges, can I point out that many of the concerns that motivated the crop trashers in the 1990s are still pertinent? The thing that conventional and organic farmers fear most is the contamination of their crops with genetic material should transgenic fields be planted nearby. As the 2009 report *Agriculture at a Crossroads* puts it: 'Despite technical solutions to prevent such gene movement... and traditional plant variety purity protocols, no method is likely to be completely effective in preventing movement of transgenes.'

We know that genetic modification of plant matter has been carried out for millennia, but let's not pretend all interference is the same. True, a version of GM allowed Mexico to become self-sufficient in wheat in the 1950s, but positive outcomes have been eclipsed by the consolidation of the seed and agrochemical industries and their use of patents. Increasingly, you hear pro-GM arguing that acceptance of GM is about increasing choices for farmers, but there are disastrous examples in developing nations where GM has proved the antithesis of choice, where promised yields haven't appeared and where farmers are trapped in a cycle of poverty and forced to buy seed each year from seed agents because they can no longer save seeds as is traditional practice (one of the GM traits in crops is that they don't produce seeds).

The top ten biotech companies control half the world's commercial seed sales. Explain to me how channelling that power into the hands of a few corporations gives us food security.

But mostly we need to stop promoting GM as a silver bullet. Last month, speaking at the 15th World Congress of Food Science and Technology in Cape Town, Sir David King, formerly Tony Blair's science adviser, could be found on his favourite hobbyhorse: 'Food insecurity in developing regions such as Africa is partially a result of the anti-GM campaign. In Europe, people might have a choice between conventional and genetically modified products. In Africa, this is not the case. Here, any food that is available is great.' Members of African GM-free groups and civil society reacted furiously.

After all, it's a 'solution' that appears to ignore that Africa's food security has been trashed by the way organisations such as the International Monetary Fund and the World Bank have pressured farmers into farming cash crops for export while simultaneously the west dumps surplus commodities on African markets.

'King is clearly not aware of the fact that Africans have common sense. Does he think we are stupid, can't think for ourselves and still listen to whatever Europeans tell us to do, like we did in the colonial era?' asked Mariam Mayet, who runs the African Centre for Biosafety, a non-profit organisation. She was at a loss to understand how GM technologies producing GM crops also for export would really help matters and, frankly, so am I.

⇨ This article first appeared in *The Observer*, 26 September 2010.

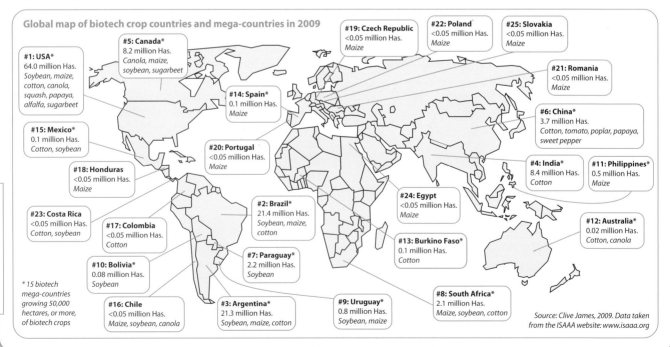

Global map of biotech crop countries and mega-countries in 2009

#1: USA*
64.0 million Has.
Soybean, maize, cotton, canola, squash, papaya, alfalfa, sugarbeet

#5: Canada*
8.2 million Has.
Canola, maize, soybean, sugarbeet

#14: Spain*
0.1 million Has.
Maize

#15: Mexico*
0.1 million Has.
Cotton, soybean

#20: Portugal
<0.05 million Has.
Maize

#18: Honduras
<0.05 million Has.
Maize

#23: Costa Rica
<0.05 million Has.
Cotton, soybean

#17: Colombia
<0.05 million Has.
Cotton

#10: Bolivia*
0.08 million Has.
Soybean

#16: Chile
<0.05 million Has.
Maize, soybean, canola

#2: Brazil*
21.4 million Has.
Soybean, maize, cotton

#7: Paraguay*
2.2 million Has.
Soybean

#3: Argentina*
21.3 million Has.
Soybean, maize, cotton

#9: Uruguay*
0.8 million Has.
Soybean, maize

#19: Czech Republic
<0.05 million Has.
Maize

#22: Poland
<0.05 million Has.
Maize

#25: Slovakia
<0.05 million Has.
Maize

#21: Romania
<0.05 million Has.
Maize

#6: China*
3.7 million Has.
Cotton, tomato, poplar, papaya, sweet pepper

#4: India*
8.4 million Has.
Cotton

#11: Philippines*
0.5 million Has.
Maize

#12: Australia*
0.02 million Has.
Cotton, canola

#24: Egypt
<0.05 million Has.
Maize

#13: Burkino Faso*
0.1 million Has.
Cotton

#8: South Africa*
2.1 million Has.
Maize, soybean, cotton

* 15 biotech mega-countries growing 50,000 hectares, or more, of biotech crops

Source: Clive James, 2009. Data taken from the ISAAA website: www.isaaa.org

THE OBSERVER

Shoppers kept in dark over GM ingredients

Millions of Britons are unwittingly eating food made using genetically modified soy, a survey of the leading grocery brands has disclosed.

By Louise Gray, Environment Correspondent

Household name brands like Cadbury Dairy Milk and Bird's Eye use milk, eggs and meat made from animals that could have been fed GM soy, the research shows.

The *Daily Telegraph* asked leading brands if they could guarantee that their products contained no ingredients from animals fed on GM soy.

The responses showed that the animal products in Hellmann's mayonnaise or Lurpak butter could be from animals fed GM soy, unless it is the organic line.

After the outcry over Frankenfoods in the 1990s, the EU ordered that supermarkets and manufacturers must label direct GM ingredients.

However there is no need to tell the consumer if GM has been used further back in the food chain.

Campaigners said allowing the livestock industry to become reliant on GM soy is letting in the controversial technology 'by the back door'.

Environmentalists claim GM soy is driving deforestation and poisoning communities in South America.

The *Telegraph* survey showed that brands including Cathedral City, Cravendale milk and Magnum ice cream use products from animals that could have been fed GM. Pet foods including Whiskas, Felix and Pedigree Chum could also include such products.

Barbara Gallani, Director of Food Safety and Science at the Food and Drink Federation, said most major brands will use meat and dairy from animals fed GM unless they are organic lines.

She said GM proteins are not passed from the soy into the animal product and the system poses no health risks.

'The increased use of biotechnology globally means that UK livestock will receive a growing proportion of GM crops in their feed,' she said. 'This is largely unavoidable, as the UK has always been reliant on imports of animal feed.'

More than three millions tonnes of soy is imported into the UK every year, a large proportion of which is GM.

The *Daily Telegraph* has already revealed that all supermarkets routinely sell food from animals reared on GM crops.

Michael Meacher, the former Labour environment minister, said there have not been enough studies carried out on the health implications of meat and dairy from animals fed GM soy.

He said food should be labelled if GM animal feed is used. 'This is a significant health and environmental issue and people are entitled to know, not have it foisted upon them.'

Caroline Lucas, the Green MP, said a recent ruling in Brussels means that shipments of GM contaminated with unauthorised seeds could be allowed into the EU.

This means that GM that has not been safety tested in Europe could end up in the UK food chain.

'This is a slippery slope, allowing crops that have not been given safety approvals to enter our food chain,' she said.

There is also 150,000 tonnes of GM soy oil sold in Britain every year, mostly used in fast food restaurants.

Caterers are supposed to tell customers if soy is used but over the past five years Trading Standards have cracked down on hundreds of hotels and pubs found to be breaking the law.

Kirtana Chandrasekaran, of Friends of the Earth, said rainforest is being cleared to make way for GM soy plantations.

The intensively farmed crops also rely on liberal use of pesticides, which can cause problems for the surrounding community.

In Paraguay there have been reports of adults and children made ill and even killed by the growing use of pesticides.

'There's a chain of destruction linking soy fields flooded with pesticides to the UK's factory farms which are polluting our countryside and giving us unhealthy food,' she said.

'The only winners are companies that produce pesticides and sell us dodgy meat. The Government can change this as part of its ongoing overhaul of farming subsidies – millions of pounds of taxpayers' money is currently spent on factory farming here in the UK.

'This money must be used to help UK farmers move away from imported soy animal feed towards healthy, planet-friendly meat and dairy.'

21 March 2011

THE TELEGRAPH

Genetically modified crops are the key to human survival, says UK's Chief Scientist

Sir John Beddington argues that moves to block GM crops on moral grounds are no longer sustainable.

By Robin McKie

Moves to block cultivation of genetically modified crops in the developing world can no longer be tolerated on ethical or moral grounds, the Government's Chief Scientist, Sir John Beddington, has warned. He said the world faced 'a perfect storm' of issues that could lead to widespread food shortages and public unrest over the next few decades. His warning comes in the wake of food riots in north Africa and rising global concern about mounting food prices.

'A number of very important factors are about to change our world,' said Beddington, an expert in population biology. 'Its population is rising by six million every month and will reach a total of around 9,000 million by 2050. At the same time, it is estimated that by 2030 more than 60% of the population will be living in cities and will no longer be involved in growing crops or raising domestic animals. And on top of that the world's population is getting more prosperous and able to pay for more food.'

Beddington said these factors indicated that the world was going to need 40% more food, 30% more water and 50% more energy by the middle of the century – at a time when climate change was starting to have serious environmental impacts on the planet, flooding coastal plains, spreading deserts and raising temperatures. 'We could cut down tropical rain forests and plant crops on the savannahs to grow more food, but that would leave us even more vulnerable to the impact of global warming and climate change. We needed these regions to help absorb carbon dioxide emissions, after all.'

Beddington said humanity had to face the fact that every means to improve food production should now be employed, including widespread use of new biotechnological techniques in farming. He stressed that no harm should be inflicted on humans or the environment. His remarks were made in advance of publication tomorrow of a major report, *The Future of Food and Farming*.

His office's report is a specific attempt to highlight moves that could halt devastation of the planet. Crucially, the report will be presented tomorrow not just to the Department of Environment, Food and Rural Affairs (Defra), but also to the Department for International Development, which directs UK foreign aid. Beddington said he would present details of his office's report in Washington next month. He also hoped it would be debated at other events, including the G8 and G20 summits.

He emphasised the role of modern biotechnological techniques, including GM crops, in the future of global food production. 'There will be no silver bullet, but it is very hard to see how it would be remotely sensible to justify not using new technologies such as GM. Just look at the problems that the world faces: water shortages and salination of existing water supplies, for example. GM crops should be able to deal with that.'

Such remarks will enrage many environmental groups, who believe it is wrong for the west to impose a technology it has developed on the third world. But Beddington was adamant about the benefits of GM crop technology. 'Around 30% of food is lost before it can be harvested because it is eaten by pests that we never learnt how to control. We cannot afford that kind of loss to continue. GM should be able to solve that problem by creating pest-resistant strains, for example. Of course, we will have to make sure these crops are properly tested; that they work; that they don't harm people; and that they don't harm the environment.'

GM crops alone would not be sufficient to hold off widespread starvation, he added. No single approach would guarantee food security for humanity for the rest of the century. A widespread approach, including the development of proper sustainability, protecting fish stocks and changes to patterns of consumption, was also critical, he said. 'This report was set up to find out if we can feed nine billion people sustainably, healthily and equitably. We can, but it will take many different approaches to crack the problem.'

Timing was crucial. 'In 2008 food prices rocketed to their highest level for decades. People said it was just a one-off, but last year what happened? Wheat prices saw their fastest ever increase. The era of declining food prices is over and we have to face that,' he added.

Almost a billion people now suffer serious food shortages and face starvation. 'It is unimaginable that in the next ten to 20 years that there will not be a worsening of that problem unless we take action now, and we have to include the widest possible range of solutions.'

⇨ This article first appeared in *The Observer*, 23 January 2011.

Can GM crops feed the hungry?

GM crops were supposed to rescue the world's one billion undernourished people. Carol Campbell discusses whether they will ever curb hunger.

By Carol Campbell

Golden Rice burst into the public imagination a decade ago, in the form of a cover article in *Time* magazine that claimed the genetically modified (GM) rice could 'save a million kids a year'.

The rice gets its golden hue from an excess of beta carotene, a precursor to vitamin A that could help half a million children who go blind each year from an often-fatal vitamin A deficiency.

But ten years later, Golden Rice is yet to cure blindness – and some believe it never will.

The public versus GM

Co-inventor Ingo Potrykus points to resistance to GM technology from pressure groups such as Greenpeace that has resulted in public and governmental resistance – including fears that rogue GM genes may contaminate wild varieties or that GM technology services corporate greed and will never help the poor.

This has led to 'excessive' regulations that have choked efforts to roll out GM crops that might feed the poor, he says.

And there are other concerns – the cost; the slowness of the research; even the idea that a 'magic bullet' approach to nutrition can provide the answer to what is, some argue, a social, cultural and economic problem.

Does this mean that all GM foods are fated never to solve the undernutrition of the poor? If public resistance dwindles, will the crops live up to their promise to help feed the world's undernourished (estimated by the UN Food and Agriculture Organization [FAO] to number one billion in 2009)?

Rowan Sage, one of the scientists working on the creation of 'C4 rice' – another engineered rice that could one day produce a radically improved yield – says it is crucial to get public approval if GM is to tackle malnutrition. The social obstacles are huge, he says, and acceptance is 'critical' for C4 rice's success.

'We have got to get buy-in because they [the hungry poor] could easily just say they don't want it,' says Sage, an ecological and evolutionary biologist at the University of Toronto, Canada, working with the Philippines-based International Rice Research Institute (IRRI) on the project.

Guillaume Gruere, a research fellow at the International Food Policy Research Institute (IFPRI) believes that most of the reasons behind the fact that there are no publicly developed GM food crops available for the poor can be traced back to resistance.

Many of the obstacles in developing countries have 'in large part resulted from influences from countries and organisations opposed to the use of GM food', Gruere says.

Some GM proponents are pessimistic that these issues will be resolved anytime soon. For example, HarvestPlus, a global programme aimed at creating more nutritious staple crops, is avoiding GM technology almost entirely and using conventional breeding instead.

But many people believe resistance will eventually wane.

Robert Ziegler, Director-General of IRRI, says it's unlikely that those opposing GM will be able to hold back the technology forever.

'In general the issue in many developing countries is that they don't have a regulatory framework to handle them [GM crops],' Ziegler told a meeting of the American Association for the Advancement of Science (AAAS) in Chicago last year (2009).

'There are pretty strong, mostly Europe-based, lobbies who oppose their use in Sub-Saharan Africa. I think that as crops that have direct benefit to consumers come on board they will eventually be accepted.'

Even Golden Rice is making some progress, he said. It is being field tested in the Philippines and the first batches may be commercially available by 2011-12.

A balanced diet

But even if opposition evaporates, there are other reasons why GM crops may fail to solve the problem of malnutrition – will tackling one particular nutritional deficiency ever bring broad success in a war that concerns so many nutrients?

For Doug Gurian-Sherman, a senior scientist in the Food & Environment Program at the US-based Union of Concerned Scientists, introducing genetically engineered crops into a developing world environment is a piecemeal approach.

'Nutritional deficiency in an impoverished community would be better addressed by encouraging and helping people eat a balanced diet that includes green leafy vegetables and protein rather than trying to pack everything into cassava or rice,' he says.

People with one deficiency often also have other nutrient deficiencies that will not be addressed by this kind of single-nutrient approach, he argues.

'I am not opposed to Golden Rice, if it works and is shown to be safe. But is it really a good use of development resources?'

Using GM to tackling a range of deficiencies in one go is the goal of the BioCassava Plus project, which aims to pack almost a full meal into cassava, a staple for 250 million people in Sub-Saharan Africa.

Turning cassava into a square meal

The GM cassava is engineered to be more nutritious on several counts and to have a longer shelf life, disease resistance and lower cyanide levels. Early versions of the plant, with one or two characteristics introduced, are undergoing field trials in Nigeria and Puerto Rico, and are set to be tested in Kenya.

The initiative is under the supervision of Richard Sayre from the Donald Danforth Plant Science Center in the United States.

Sayre rejects Gurian-Sherman's argument: 'We know our cassava can help people,' he says. 'Initial estimates are that, in the first round of production, 35,000 lives will be saved in Nigeria. The long-term impact is millions of lives saved.'

Such claims are beguiling, but what about the cost when there's a limited international pot from which to fund nutrition?

Gurian-Sherman argues that the costs are so high that efforts should go elsewhere. A new biotechnology crop, he says, could cost up to US$100 million to produce (excluding regulatory costs) while the same crop improved through traditional methods would cost US$1 million.

In the case of C4 rice, the development costs are vast, says Sage.

'It is extremely expensive work,' he told the AAAS meeting. 'In order to create a sustained programme it needs US$10 million a year.'

But, he argued, 'it's cheap compared with the benefits'. C4 rice could, he says, increase yield by 50 per cent – and the benefits of that are in the trillions of dollars.

The C4 project must therefore be viewed in the long term to understand its benefits. It will take two to three decades to come to fruition but could help solve the food challenges of 2050, he said.

So perhaps by 2050, with biosafety frameworks in place, resistance to GM subdued by the growing trouble of world hunger, and comprehensive GM solutions that solve a host of deficiencies in a single plant, GM might solve the problem of malnutrition?

Is GM a crude solution?

But there is still one major objection – that the problem of poor nutrition is so complex that it is crude to think it can be solved by GM.

The poor don't get enough food for a number of reasons: infrastructure, such as poor roads along which to take their goods to market; lack of fertiliser; lack of training in farming methods.

The rise of monocultures has reduced the variety of their diets. Land is distributed inefficiently or unfairly with the poor pushed onto unproductive land – and this requires legal reform followed by implementation. Popping a gene into a tomato is not going to solve these problems, it is argued.

Andrea Roberto Sonnino, a senior agricultural research officer at the Research and Extension Unit of the FAO in Italy, says: 'GM can contribute to improved nutrition but we have to consider that nutrition is a result of many social, cultural, economic and political factors.'

To improve the nutrition of the poor, action cannot be limited to the improvement of the nutritional quality of a particular crop, he says.

Bonnie McClafferty, head of development and communications at HarvestPlus agrees.

'The enormity and complexity of the problem means we need [many] solutions to be made available, including diversifying diets, commercially fortifying foods, administering nutrition supplements, and breeding crops to be rich in vitamins and minerals,' she says.

'While the amounts of desired nutrient in food crops can be enhanced through conventional breeding, where these nutrients are not found in parent breeding lines, or cannot be increased in the amount needed to improve nutrition, GM foods can be seen as part of the solution.'

'GM technology may well be able to go beyond where conventional plant breeding can take us.'

Perhaps, as with the approach to climate change, the solution lies in a web of interventions of which GM may be one.

And, like climate change, it may be foolhardy to ignore any of them.

Carol Campbell is a freelance science journalist based in Oudtshoorn, South Africa.
20 January 2010

⇨ The above information is reprinted with kind permission from SciDev.net. Visit their website at www. scidev.net for more information on this and other related topics.

© SciDev.net

Genetic modification: glow-in-the-dark lifesavers or mutant freaks?

As Home Office statistics reveal a 10% rise in the use of genetically modified animals for research, scientists appear to be divided about their usefulness.

By Robin McKie

At first glance, the creation of a chicken that glows in the dark seems a disturbing and unnecessary one. With a jellyfish gene inserted into its DNA, a hen modified this way acquires the power to fluoresce in a bright green hue when illuminated with blue light – an unsettling ability, to say the least. After all, who needs poultry that can shine a light on itself? More important, why go to the trouble of mixing the DNA of two such dissimilar creatures in the first place?

What gives the insertion of a piece of DNA from one living being into another such an advantage for scientists?

It is an important question that has recently been reflected in headlines that followed the release of Home Office figures which show there was a dramatic rise in the creation of genetically modified animals in laboratories in 2009. In total, 1.5 million experiments on GM animals were carried out, a rise of 143,000 from the previous year. At the same time, there was a corresponding decrease in experiments on 'natural' animals.

In other words, more and more scientists are now relying on the use of GM animals, as opposed to unmodified ones, for their research. But what gives the insertion of a piece of DNA from one living being into another such an advantage for scientists? After all, inserting invertebrate genes into mammals, and vice versa, is not easy. It also makes the public uncomfortable and raises the hackles of animal rights organisations. Yet it has become the standard route for researchers. Why?

Consider that glowing poultry. Fluorescent chickens were developed by scientists at Edinburgh University's Roslin Institute, the zoological research organisation responsible for the creation of Dolly the sheep. As we have noted, the technique involves putting jellyfish genes into the DNA of a chick so that it makes a green, fluorescent protein. 'The protein itself does not affect the chicken in any way but it is a very useful tool for looking at the very early embryos,' says Roslin researcher Professor Helen Sang.

The crucial point is that chicks are extremely useful for studying embryo development because their growth takes place inside an egg which can be kept in an incubator and studied fairly easily. By contrast, a mammal foetus gestates inside the uterus of its mother, making it far harder for researchers to monitor physiological changes. Thus the chick provides us with a key model for understanding the development of early embryos for all vertebrates, including humans. But the technique had been pushed to its limits by scientists – until the arrival of the GM mutant. This allows scientists to tinker with the way in which an embryo develops and so reveal processes that were previously obscured.

'You can take a sample of cells from a green embryo and then put them into a normal embryo,' says Sang. 'You can then watch and see what organ that group of cells develops into because that tissue will have a green fluorescence. For example, if this part of the chick embryo develops into stem cells, that tells us whether other animals, including humans, have stem cells in that part of their embryos and will therefore provide us with important basic biological insights.' In other words, stem-cell science can get a boost from the glowing green chicken.

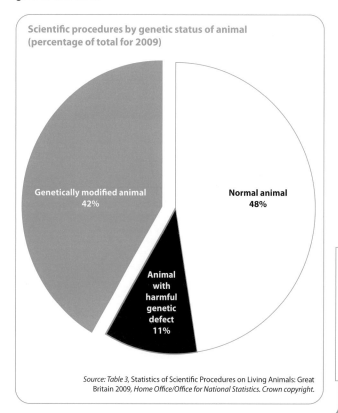

Scientific procedures by genetic status of animal (percentage of total for 2009)

Genetically modified animal 42%

Normal animal 48%

Animal with harmful genetic defect 11%

Source: Table 3, Statistics of Scientific Procedures on Living Animals: Great Britain 2009, *Home Office/Office for National Statistics. Crown copyright.*

THE OBSERVER

In fact, the chicken turns out to be a popular target for modification. Roslin scientists are also working on a strain that can express therapeutic proteins in the whites of eggs. In particular, they are working on whites in which the hen expresses antibodies that can block viruses which cause enteric – i.e. gut – diseases. Thus it may be possible one day to cook omelettes that could prevent us succumbing to disease, though most scientists envisage a slightly different route in which GM egg whites are dried out before their antibodies are removed and administered separately.

But what geneticists have not developed, insists Sang, is the featherless chicken. This animal is often held up as the ultimate GM horror, created so that farmers will be saved the effort of having to pluck feathers before poultry are sold to supermarkets. In fact, the partly featherless chicken is a species containing a natural mutation called naked neck which is becoming popular in hot countries, such as Israel, where the animals can be kept cool without a full feather covering.

Nevertheless, there are other criticisms of the use of GM animals, as the watchdog group GeneWatch has pointed out. Its director Helen Wallace says the rise in the use of GM animals reveals a disturbing trend: the 'genetification' of biology. 'There are undoubtedly some legitimate uses of GM animals but this blanket rise is worrying and bears little relation to reality,' she says. Wallace points to the widespread creation of animals – mice in particular – that have been genetically altered so they succumb to human conditions such as obesity and cancer. These mutants are then used to test drugs that could counter these ailments in humans.

'The trouble with this approach is that it stresses the use of medical intervention for ailments that also have clear environmental causes,' says Wallace. 'Too much

food and exposure to pollutants are also clear causes of cancer and obesity, but these are being ignored because of our obsession with genetics. In fact, in many conditions, genes have only a small role to play in the causation of the disease, yet we have become fixated on trying to tackle them, to the detriment of other, more fruitful approaches.'

This point is acknowledged – partially – by genetic engineers. 'We do concentrate a lot on genetic approaches to disease, but that is because we geneticists are only now catching up with other sciences,' says Luke Alphey, head of Oxitec, an Oxford University spin-off genetics company. 'For the first time, we have got the tools to do this sort of thing. And in any case, a disease is generally a combination of genetic and environmental causes. So the more we learn about genetic influences the more we will know about their environmental influences as well.'

Alphey and his colleagues are working on techniques to prevent mosquitoes from spreading dengue fever, a severe, sometimes fatal viral illness that affects between 50 to 100 million people a year. 'We have created a strain of genetically modified male mosquitoes of the *Aedes aegypti* species, the one responsible for spreading dengue fever,' he says. 'These males produce offspring that do not develop fully. So they block the appearance of new *A. aegypti* mosquitoes. Released into the wild, which we hope to do in a few years, these GM mosquitoes should eradicate *A. aegypti* populations and halt new dengue fever cases. If the technique works, we will have demonstrated just how powerful and useful this technology can be.'

⇨ This article first appeared in *The Observer*, 8 August 2010.

GE salmon critics raise 'Trojan gene' spectre

Information from the Los Angeles Times.

By Andy Zajac

The [US] Food and Drug Administration's public comment period for labelling requirements for a genetically engineered salmon ended not so quietly, with a flurry of press releases leading up to Monday's deadline.

They included an announcement by a group of lawmakers from Alaska and the Northwest that would prohibit FDA approval of a GE salmon, or require that it be labelled as genetically engineered in the event regulators approved the fish.

A key element of the last-minute volley was a letter from a dozen environmental, science and consumer groups to FDA Commissioner Margaret Hamburg urging her to look carefully at possible adverse ecological consequences as it evaluates a Massachusetts firm's application for a GE salmon for human consumption. If approved, the salmon would be the first GE food animal.

'We anticipate that a comprehensive [review] will show that the [GE] salmon pose a threat to wild salmon populations and the health of marine and freshwater ecosystems around the world,' the letter states.

The AquaBounty Technologies' AquaAdvantage salmon reaches market weight in about half the time of a regular North Atlantic salmon.

The letter reminds the FDA of the need to consider a worst-case scenario: that the GE salmon, which is to be raised in closed, land-based facilities, will escape and inflict unknown consequences on the environment.

It leans heavily on perhaps the most hotly disputed evidence in the GE salmon debate, the so-called Trojan Gene effect, in which a specific genetic advantage – in this case the AquaBounty salmon's ability to grow faster – enables it to outcompete unaltered salmon, leading to their demise.

The letter states: 'If salmon genetically engineered to grow faster than wild fish escape confinement, they will threaten the health and survival of wild salmon populations. According to research from Purdue University, if just 60 GE fish were released into a wild population of 60,000, the wild population could be extinct within 40 generations. This result is driven by the 'Trojan gene effect' in which specific fitness advantages in an otherwise less-fit organism result in gene spread and an ultimate weakening and eventual collapse of the species.

Not so, says the author of the Trojan Gene hypothesis, William Muir, an animal science professor at Purdue who has been yelling loudly, to little effect so far, that his work is being misrepresented by the GE salmon's opponents.

Muir said the assumption at the time of the study in 1999 was that a GE salmon would grow faster and bigger and that its size would be an unbeatable advantage in mating.

But AquaBounty salmon don't get any bigger than ordinary salmon, they just reach full size faster, so any size advantage they have is temporary.

More importantly, Muir said that studies show that transgenic salmon are lousy at the courtship required for mating.

On 20 September, Muir told the FDA Veterinary Medicine Advisory Committee evaluating the GE salmon that 'the data conclusively shows that there is no Trojan Gene effect as expected. The data in fact suggest that the transgene will be purged by natural selection. In other words the risk of harm here is low.'

In an email to Greenspace, Muir said that: 'The concept of a Trojan Gene entering a population due to mating advantage is now known to be an urban myth. The myth is that females like males who are larger. In fact, females like males who have good courtship displays. Who would have thought the jocks would loose [sic] out to the nerds when it came to attracting girls!! Thus because the fish grows faster does not automatically result in the Trojan Gene. It is like saying "If the sun were to nova all the people of the earth would be killed," but then reporting that "scientist says the sun will kill all the people of the earth". The sin of omission is as great as the sin of insertion.'

Muir notes that his own research states that: 'With nearly continuous access to females, [GE] males courted them frequently; however, the vast majority of courtship attempts ended in female rejection displays.'

There's no indication of when the FDA, which has been mulling the GE salmon for more than a decade, will make a decision, though the agency has made a preliminary determination that the fish is safe for people to eat and does not pose a significant environmental risk.

The FDA's veterinary advisory committee in September recommended further study of the fish's potential to trigger allergies or other health problems in some consumers.

While the panel did not make a recommendation either to approve or reject the fish, comments and questions seemed to convey a sense that the fish is safe for human consumption, though several panellists expressed concern about the small sample sizes of some studies.

26 November 2010

LOS ANGELES TIMES

KEY FACTS

⇨ GM allows chosen individual genes to be transferred from one organism into another, including genes between non-related species. Such methods can be used to create GM crop plants. The technology is also sometimes called 'modern biotechnology', 'gene technology', 'recombinant DNA technology' or 'genetic engineering'. (page 1)

⇨ After 13 years of being consumed by hundreds of millions of people, there is no substantiated evidence of any health effect from eating GM food products. (page 2)

⇨ GM foods first came on the market in the early 1990s and have created controversy ever since. Pro-GM scientists see them as a way to feed the world, while other scientists and environmentalists cite possible safety issues, ecological and health concerns. (page 3)

⇨ The only GM crop licensed for growing on a commercial scale in Europe is unsuitable for UK conditions and is grown in northern Spain. (page 5)

⇨ Every year more than 300 million acres of GM are planted around the world. (page 5)

⇨ Genetic modification can be used to reduce the amount of pesticide needed by altering a plant's DNA so it can resist the particular insect pests that attack it. Genetic modification can also be used to give crops immunity to plant viruses or to improve the nutritional value of a plant. (page 6)

⇨ About 98 million hectares out of a global GM crop area of 125 million hectares were grown in just three countries, by large-scale farmers: the United States (62.5 million), Argentina (21 million) and Brazil (15 million). (page 9)

⇨ The planting of genetically modified crops has surged, particularly in developing countries, because of the global food crisis, according to a report. (page 10)

⇨ The European Commission has authorised cultivation of a new GM crop for the first time in 12 years, approving BASF's genetically modified potato Amflora for industrial use. The move has given GM advocates hope that a backlog of applications for other GM crops will also be authorised. (page 11)

⇨ For thousands of years farmers and plant breeders have been changing the genetic makeup of crops to improve characteristics like size, resistance to disease and taste. (page 17)

⇨ Two-thirds of people in the UK want GM crops to be kept out of the food chain, a survey by Friends of the Earth has revealed. (page 18)

⇨ Despite the promises, GM has not increased the yield potential of any commercialised crops. In fact, studies show that the most widely grown GM crop, GM soya, has suffered reduced yields. (page 23)

⇨ Our everyday diet consists of around 6,000 different chemicals which we are perfectly able to deal with through digestion. It is very unlikely that GM crops are going to alter the fundamentals of nature and expose us to anything new. (page 27)

⇨ In the UK, agriculture accounts for 7% of all carbon emissions; the use of GM technology can help in reducing the carbon footprint and environmental impact of farming in a number of ways. (page 29)

⇨ Household name brands like Cadbury Dairy Milk and Bird's Eye use milk, eggs and meat made from animals that could have been fed GM soy, research shows. (page 33)

⇨ Almost a billion people now suffer serious food shortages and face starvation. (page 34)

⇨ Home Office figures show there was a dramatic rise in the creation of genetically modified animals in laboratories in 2009. In total, 1.5 million experiments on GM animals were carried out, a rise of 143,000 from the previous year. At the same time, there was a corresponding decrease in experiments on 'natural' animals. (page 37)

Biodiversity

This term refers to the number and variety of different species among living organisms. There are concerns that the crossing of genes between different species through genetic modification would result in decreased biodiversity.

Biofuel

A gaseous, liquid or solid fuel derived from a biological source, e.g. ethanol, rapeseed oil. Some scientists claim that GM would be a useful tool in the quest to produce biofuels which would be beneficial for the environment.

Biotechnology

Sometimes the term 'biotechnology' is used to describe genetic modification. This also has a wider meaning: using micro-organisms or biological techniques to process waste or produce useful compounds, such as vaccines.

Cross-contamination

Sometimes, genetically modified material can be passed unintentionally between plant crops: this is called cross-contamination. It can result in the presence of GM substances in what is thought to be a GM-free crop, and is therefore one concern raised by consumers who want to be able to make informed choices about whether or not to eat GM food.

DNA

DNA stands for deoxyribonucleic acid. It is the genetic material contained in the cells of all living things and it carries the information that allows organisms to function, repair and reproduce themselves. Every cell of plants, micro-organisms (such as bacteria), animals and people contain many thousands of different genes, which are made of DNA. These genes determine the characteristics, or genetic make-up, of every living thing, including the food we eat. When we eat any food, we are eating the genes and breaking down the DNA present in the food.

Genes

A gene is an instruction and each of our cells contains tens of thousands of these instructions. In humans, these instructions work together to determine everything from our eye colour to our risk of heart disease. The reason we all have slightly different characteristics is that before we are born our parents' genes get shuffled about at random. The same principles apply to other animals and plants.

Genetic modification

May also be called modern biotechnology, gene technology, recombinant DNA technology or genetic engineering. Scientists are able to modify genes in order to produce different characteristics in an organism than it would have produced naturally. GM techniques allow specific genes to be transferred from one organism to another, including between non-related species. This technology might be used, for example, to produce plants which are more resistant to pesticides, which have a higher nutritional value, or which produce a greater crop yield. Those in favour of GM say that this could bring real benefits to food producers and consumers. Those against GM feel it is risky as scientists do not have the knowledge to 'play God' with the food we eat.

Genomics

An organism's genome can be defined as all its genetic material packed together. Genomics is the science of genomes – more specifically, their sequencing, mapping, analysis, study and manipulation.

Nanotechnology

Nanotechnology covers those man-made materials or objects that are about a thousand times smaller than the microtechnology we use routinely, such as the silicon chips of computers. (definition from the Independent)

Selective breeding

Human beings have been modifying the genes of biological organisms for centuries through selective breeding: choosing individual plants and animals with particular traits, like fast growth rates or good seed production, and breeding them with others to produce the most desirable combination of characteristics. However, unlike genetic modification, this can happen only within closely-related species.

allergen-free nuts 29
Amflora potato 11
amino acids and GM food 20
animal feed, GM ingredients 8, 24
animals, genetic modification 3, 13–14, 37–8
   chickens 14, 37–8
   salmon 31, 39
AquaBounty GM salmon 31, 39

bananas, fungus resistance 1
BASF, Amflora potato 11
bio-fortification 19
biodiversity and GM crops 20–21, 28
biofuels 22
biomaterials 21
biotech companies 3–4, 24
bird flu resistance, GM chickens 14
Bt plants 3, 21

C4 rice 20, 36
carbon dioxide control and GM crops 20, 22
carbon footprint, GM food 29
cassava 36
cheese production 8
chickens
   resistance to bird flu 14
   used in GM research 37–8
consumer attitudes to GM foods 29–30, 31
consumer information and GM ingredients 33
contamination of crops 24, 26

developing countries, planting of GM crops 10
disease resistance, GM crops 29
DNA 7

environmental benefits of GM crops 20, 22, 29
EU and nanofoods 16
European Commission
   approval of GM crop 11
   plan to relax GM crop restrictions 12
European Food Safety Authority (EFSA) 7

farmers, impact of GM crops 24, 28
first generation GM plants 2
fluorescent chickens, research applications 37–8
food, GM *see* GM foods
food safety 2, 24
Food Standards Agency, UK 7
food supply and GM crops 19, 23–4, 32, 34–6

gene mapping 13
generations of GM plants 1–2
genetic modification
   applications 6, 19–22, 37–8
   arguments against 3–4, 5, 17
   arguments for 2, 3, 17
   definition 1, 3

and food production *see* GM foods
   method 14
   risks 17
   testing 1
global warming mitigation and GM crops 22
GM crops 1–2
   arguments for and against 5, 9–10, 17, 34
   extent of cultivation 9, 10   risks 27–8
   and food supply 19, 23–4, 32, 34–6
GM foods 5–8
   arguments against 23–4, 31–2
   effects on health 5, 8, 19–20
   public attitudes 18, 29–30
   safety 2
   safety testing 1, 7
GM generations 1–2
golden rice 19, 29, 35
Government policy on GM 5
greenhouse gas emissions and GM crops 22

health benefits of GM crops 19–20, 29

insects, effects of GM crops 27
intellectual property and GM seeds 3–4

labelling
   GM foods 8
   nanomaterials 16

mapping genes 13
medical applications
   of GM plants 21–2
   of transgenic animals 13
Monsanto 3–4

nanofoods 15
nanotechnology 15–16
nutrition and GM crops 35–6

patents on seeds 3–4
pesticide production, Bt plants 3, 21
pesticide use and GM crops 23
pharmaceutical production 21–2
potatoes 11
public attitudes to GM foods 18, 29–30

research uses of GM animals 37–8
risks
   GM crops 27–8
   nanotechnology 16

safety, GM food 2, 24
   testing 1, 7
salmon 31, 39
second generation GM plants 2
soil erosion reduction and GM crops 20

ACKNOWLEDGEMENTS

The publisher is grateful for permission to reproduce the following material.

While every care has been taken to trace and acknowledge copyright, the publisher tenders its apology for any accidental infringement or where copyright has proved untraceable. The publisher would be pleased to come to a suitable arrangement in any such case with the rightful owner.

Chapter One: GM Trends

The science behind GM crops, © Agricultural Biotechnology Council 2009, *GM – the facts,* © Debate Your Plate, *GM food Q&A,* © Telegraph Media Group Limited 2010, *Production of GM foods,* © Crown copyright is reproduced with the permission of Her Majesty's Stationery Office, *GM crops ten years on: hope, hype and reality,* © Economic and Social Research Council (ESRC), *GM crops flourishing in developing world, says report,* © SciDev.net, *EC approves first GM crop in a decade,* © Royal Society of Chemistry, *EU angers all camps with move to relax GM crop restrictions,* © BusinessGreen, *Animal genetics and biotechnology,* © Farming and Countryside Education, *GM chickens breakthrough to prevent spread of bird flu,* © BBSRC, *Is nanotechnology the new GM?,* © Ethical Consumer.

Chapter Two: The Debate

The GM debate in context, © Institute of Ideas Debating Matters Competition, *Two-thirds want GM to be kept off their plate,* © Friends of the Earth, *How does biotechnology address current human and environmental challenges?,* © EuropaBio, *Ten reasons why we don't need GM foods,* © bangmfood.org, *Why can't we make a decision about the genetic modification of foods and crops?,* © British Science Association, *GM crops – the risks explained,* © UK Agriculture, *Consumer benefits of GM crops,* © Agricultural Biotechnology Council 2009, *Just because GM is gaining popularity doesn't make it right,* © Guardian News and Media Limited 2010, *Shoppers kept in dark over GM ingredients,* © Telegraph Media Group Limited 2010, *Genetically modified crops are the key to human survival, says UK's Chief Scientist,* © Guardian News and Media Limited 2010, *Can GM crops feed the hungry?,* © SciDev.net, *Genetic modification: glow-in-the-dark lifesavers or mutant freaks?,* © Guardian News and Media Limited 2010, *GE salmon critics raise 'Trojan gene' spectre,* © 2010, Los Angeles Times, reprinted with permission.

Illustrations

Pages 1, 3, 23, 30: Don Hatcher; pages 4, 8, 25, 31: Simon Kneebone; pages 5, 12: Bev Aisbett; pages 11, 21, 27, 38: Angelo Madrid.

Cover photography

Left: © Andrew W. M. Beierle. Centre: © Ozecha. Right: © Typofi.

Additional acknowledgements

And with thanks to the Independence team: Mary Chapman, Sandra Dennis and Jan Sunderland.

Lisa Firth
Cambridge
April, 2011

ASSIGNMENTS

The following tasks aim to help you think through the issues surrounding genetic modification and provide a better understanding of the topic.

1 'After 13 years of being consumed by hundreds of millions of people, there is no substantiated evidence of any health effect from eating GM food products.' Does this prove that genetic modification is safe? Discuss your views with a partner.

2 Conduct a poll within your year group to find out about their views on GM food. How many would be prepared to try GM food? Do they think GM food should be sold in supermarkets, and if so, do they think it should be clearly labelled? Write a summary of your findings, including graphs to illustrate the results.

3 'This house believes that genetically modified crops are the only solution if we are to solve the world food crisis and eradicate hunger for good.' Debate this motion in two groups, with one arguing in favour and the other against.

4 Go through the articles in this book and try to ascertain the writer's standpoint on GM for each one, classifying each as 'Pro-GM', 'Anti-GM' or 'Neutral'. Summarise briefly the main arguments in each article until you have a bulleted list of views both for and against genetic modification. Which do you find more convincing?

5 Find out about biofuel. How could GM crops contribute to developing biofuels? What are the possible advantages for the environment? Are there any disadvantages?

6 Do you think genetically modifying crops and animals for the purpose of producing medicines to cure disease is more or less ethically justifiable than modifying them for food? Explain your answer.

7 Find out more about Monsanto, one of the biggest biotechnology corporations which is rumoured to own 90% of the world's market in GM seeds, looking in particular at their use of patents. Write an article about their work, including what their critics have to say about them and how the company has responded.

8 What is selective breeding and how is it done? In what ways does it differ from genetic modification?

9 Find out about the creation of in vitro meat. Could this help to address the food crisis? Would you try it?

10 It is currently the law that any GM ingredients in our food must be labelled: however, there is no obligation to label food which has been produced from animals fed on GM crops, which some claim undermines consumer choice regarding GM. Design a label which could be displayed on products created from animals given GM feed.

11 Imagine you are creating the branding for a new lobby group, which will campaign either against GM foods or in favour of them. Design a memorable name, logo and slogan for your organisation and incorporate them into a homepage design for your new website.

12 Read a summary of the book 'Brave New World' by Aldous Huxley. Although this book was written before the discovery of DNA, it indicates the author's fears if the study of eugenics were to get out of hand. Write your own story about the future of genetic modification. You may choose to create a future which has been improved by GM food or made worse, depending on your views.

13 Read *GM crops ten years on: hope, hype and reality* on pages 9-10. Find out more about the history of genetic modification. Create a timeline to show how GM foods were developed and implemented and any turning points in public attitudes towards them, both in the UK and internationally.

14 Carry out a case study of Golden Rice, a GM crop fortified with vitamin A. Gather together all the information you can on this crop from a variety of sources, both for and against. Use your findings to write an article about the potential advantages and disadvantages of Golden Rice, including quotes to support your points.

15 Read *Genetic modification: glow-in-the-dark life-savers or mutant freaks?* on pages 37-38. Is it right to genetically modify animals for use in medical testing? Discuss your views with a partner.